MATH TRAILBLAZERS™

Grade 4

Unit Resource Guide
Unit 7

Patterns in Multiplication

SECOND EDITION

A Mathematical Journey Using Science and Language Arts

KENDALL/HUNT PUBLISHING COMPANY
4050 Westmark Drive   Dubuque, Iowa 52002

A TIMS® Curriculum
University of Illinois at Chicago

UIC The University of Illinois
at Chicago

The original edition was based on work supported by the National Science Foundation under grant
No. MDR 9050226 and the University of Illinois at Chicago. Any opinions, findings, and conclusions
or recommendations expressed in this publication are those of the author(s) and do not necessarily
reflect the views of the granting agencies.

LETTER HOME

Patterns in Multiplication

Date: _____

Dear Family Member:

Students develop their understanding of multiplication using a paper-and-pencil method called the all-partials method. In this method, every step in a multiplication problem is written down. This is slightly different from the compact method, which leaves some steps unrecorded. For example:

All-Partials Method

```
  39    (In this method,
 ×6     6 × 9 is recorded
  54    as 54, and 6 × 30
 180    is recorded as 180.
 234    The addition is done last.)
```

Compact Method

```
   5
  39    (In this method, the 4 ones
 ×6     from 54 are recorded,
 234    and the 5 tens are written
        above to be added to 180.)
```

The all-partials method encourages students to keep a clear record of all the partial calculations. This helps students visualize how the place-value system operates in multiplication and helps students learn to multiply larger numbers. Later, students will be introduced to the more traditional compact method as a shortcut.

Estimation is an important part of this unit. Students use patterns to calculate with tens and hundreds to make mental calculations easier. Rounding numbers to the nearest tens', hundreds', or thousands' place is one way of selecting a convenient number to use in estimating. You can help your child by encouraging estimation. For example, in the grocery store, ask your child questions such as: "About how much will two loaves of bread cost?" or "Will $10.00 be enough to pay for three gallons of milk?"

This unit continues the review of the multiplication facts. Students will work on the last six facts: 4×6, 4×7, 4×8, 6×7, 6×8, and 7×8. Help your child study these facts with the *Triangle Flash Cards.*

Estimating the cost of two books is one of the real-world situations in this unit.

Sincerely,

_____

UNIT OUTLINE

Patterns in Multiplication

Pacing Suggestions

- This unit develops mental math, estimation, and paper-and-pencil skills for multiplication. Use the recommended session numbers for each lesson as a guide. It is not necessary to stop until students master each skill—especially paper-and-pencil procedures—as students will revisit them in later units, particularly in Unit 11.

- The Daily Practice and Problems includes review of the last group of multiplication facts. This group is called the Last Six Facts (4×6, 4×7, 4×8, 6×7, 6×8, 7×8). These facts are often the most difficult for students to learn. Allow time for students to practice, share strategies, and use them to solve problems. Systematic review of the facts is also found in the *Grade 4 Facts Resource Guide*. Use this guide if your pacing schedule is significantly different from the recommended schedule.

Components Key: SG = Student Guide, DAB = Discovery Assignment Book, AB = Adventure Book, URG = Unit Resource Guide, and DPP = Daily Practice and Problems

	Sessions	Description	Supplies
LESSON 1 **Order of Operations** SG pages 180–183 URG pages 26–33 DPP A–B	1–2	**ACTIVITY:** Students learn the conventional order for carrying out basic arithmetic operations. A game, *Operation Target*, provides practice with this order and basic math facts.	• calculators • scissors • envelopes
LESSON 2 **Divisibility Rules** SG pages 184–189 URG pages 34–46 DPP C–F	2	**ACTIVITY:** Students find ways to determine whether a multidigit number is evenly divisible by 2, 3, 5, 6, 9, or 10.	• calculators • blue and red crayons or colored pencils • blue and red overhead markers
LESSON 3 **Oh, No! My Calculator Is Broken** SG pages 190–192 URG pages 47–61 DPP G–L	3	**ASSESSMENT ACTIVITY:** Students use the order of operations and a "broken" calculator to generate the numbers from 1 to 50. **ASSESSMENT PAGE:** *The Broken Calculator*, Unit Resource Guide, page 60.	• calculators

	Sessions	Description	Supplies
LESSON 4 **Multiplying by 10s** SG pages 193–196 URG pages 62–69 DPP M–P	2	**ACTIVITY:** Students explore patterns when multiplying 1-digit numbers by multidigit numbers ending in zeros. Finding unknowns in number sentences is introduced.	• base-ten pieces • calculators
LESSON 5 **Multiplication** SG pages 197–201 URG pages 70–77 DPP Q–V	3–4	**ACTIVITY:** Students are introduced to the all-partials method of multiplication.	• base-ten pieces
LESSON 6 **Estimation** SG pages 202–206 URG pages 78–85 DPP W–Z	2	**ACTIVITY:** Students explore computational estimation. Students develop techniques for finding convenient numbers for estimation.	
LESSON 7 **Multiplying Round Numbers** SG pages 207–210 URG pages 86–92 DPP AA–BB	1	**ACTIVITY:** Students use patterns to multiply multidigit numbers ending in zeros. They practice estimation. **ASSESSMENT PAGE:** *Multiplication*, Unit Resource Guide, page 90.	• calculators
LESSON 8 **A Camping Trip** SG pages 211–213 URG pages 93–97 DPP CC–DD	1–2	**ACTIVITY:** Students solve word problems centered around a camping trip.	

CONNECTIONS

A current list of connections is available at www.mathtrailblazers.com.

Software

- *Ice Cream Truck* provides practice with problem solving, money skills, and arithmetic operations.
- *Math Arena* is a collection of math activities that reinforces many math concepts.
- *Math Munchers Deluxe* provides practice with basic facts and identifying factors and multiples in an arcade-like game.
- *Math Workshop Deluxe* develops math facts proficiency.
- *Mighty Math Calculating Crew* provides practice with number operations and money skills.
- *Number Sense—How the West Was One + Three × Four* provides practice with the order of operations.

PREPARING FOR UPCOMING LESSONS

In Unit 9, students will cut up boxes to explore three-dimensional geometry. Have students bring in small boxes for a class collection.

BACKGROUND

Patterns in Multiplication

This unit includes work with multiplication, the order of operations, facts, divisibility rules, and estimation strategies.

Order of Operations

The unit begins with an exploration of the order of operations. Students learn that in number sentences, the standard convention is that multiplication and division are completed before addition and subtraction. Thus, the solution to $2 + 3 \times 5$ is 17. In particular, students must learn to be careful when using a calculator. All scientific calculators and some nonscientific calculators incorporate the order of operations. Other nonscientific calculators do not follow the order of operations and would do the calculation from left to right giving the incorrect solution of 25 to the problem $2 + 3 \times 5$. In this unit, students learn that the conventional order of operations assigns priorities to operations and specifies how operations of the same priority are to be executed.

Divisibility

In order to further develop children's number sense, a lesson on divisibility rules is included in this unit. Students learn that numbers that end in even numbers are divisible by 2; numbers that end in 5 and 0 are divisible by 5; and numbers that end in 0 are divisible by 10. Although students may be acquainted with these ideas, discussing them increases awareness and gives students new tools for working with numbers.

Divisibility rules for 3 and 9 are often new to students. Students learn that if the sum of the digits of a number is divisible by 3, the number is divisible by 3. Similarly, if the sum of the digits of a number is divisible by 9, then the number is divisible by 9. For example, the number 8136 is divisible by 9 and by 3 because $8 + 1 + 3 + 6 = 18$—a multiple of both 9 and 3. Students are also introduced to the fact that a number that is divisible by both 2 and 3 is also divisible by 6. By studying divisibility, students develop a better understanding of the operations of multiplication and division and how they relate to one another. Fluency with the multiplication and division facts is also enhanced.

Multiplying by Numbers Ending in Zero

Patterns formed when multiplying by numbers ending in zero are an important aspect of multiplication. In this unit, students use calculators to find products such as 3×20, 3×200, 3×2000, etc. From these experiences, students will discover that the number of zeros in the product depends on the sum of the zeros in the multiplicands. Facility with multiplying numbers with ending zeros is an important skill for mental math (Hazekamp, 1986). Research has also shown that it is related to students' ability to estimate (Rubenstein, 1985).

Estimation

Estimation can be broken up into four major categories: computational estimation, estimation involving measures, estimation involving error in experiments and predictions, and estimation involving the number of objects in a set. Previously, students explored estimating measures and estimating the number of objects in a set. (They explored computational estimation for addition and subtraction in Unit 6.) Students also encountered error in estimates in their laboratory investigations. In this unit, we will focus mainly on computational estimates for multiplication. Such estimates involve first replacing the original numbers with more convenient numbers and then doing the computation mentally with these numbers. This type of estimating is an important life skill.

Researchers stress that estimation skills should be developed slowly, so that students can be flexible in the strategies they use for estimation, rather than resorting to rote memorization of specific procedures (Sowder, 1992). Estimation and number sense are closely connected. A child who has a good number sense will have the means and confidence to estimate and decide whether an answer is reasonable. (National Research Council, 2001) Research also indicates that good estimators often have a good understanding of place value (Reys, et al., 1982). The TIMS Tutor: *Estimation, Accuracy, and Error* contains more discussion on the topic.

The All-Partials Method of Multiplication

The *Math Trailblazers*™ curriculum uses a variation of the traditional multiplication algorithm. In this method, which we call the **all-partials algorithm,** every partial product is recorded on a separate line. Ending zeros are included in the partial products.

For example, 7×346 is the sum of 7×300, 7×40, and 7×6. We can record this in vertical form as:

$$
\begin{array}{r}
346 \\
\times 7 \\
\hline
42 \\
280 \\
2100 \\
\hline
2422
\end{array}
$$

The rationale for using the all-partials algorithm is threefold. First, children develop a better understanding of the concept of multiplication and a better understanding of the algorithm as a concise paper-and-pencil method for doing multiplication. Second, the problem of not lining up numbers properly is alleviated. Finally, the all-partials algorithm provides practice with problems like 7×300, an essential skill for estimation. Refer to the TIMS Tutor: *Arithmetic* for more discussion of algorithms. If children have learned the traditional method, do not discourage its use by those students who understand how it works and are proficient with it.

Resources

- Hazekamp, D.W. "Components of Mental Multiplying." In *Estimation and Mental Computation: 1986 Yearbook,* Harold L. Schoen and Marilyn M. Zweng (eds.). National Council of Teachers of Mathematics, Reston, VA, 1986.

- National Research Council. "Developing Proficiency with Whole Numbers." In *Adding It Up: Helping Children Learn Mathematics,* J. Kilpatrick, J. Swafford, and B. Findell, eds. National Academy Press, Washington, DC, 2001.

- Reys, R.E., J.F. Rybolt, B.J. Bestgen, and J.W. Wyatt, "Processes Used by Good Computational Estimators." *Journal for Research in Mathematics Education,* 13, 183–201, 1982.

- Rubenstein, R.N. "Computational Estimation and Related Mathematical Skill." *Journal for Research in Mathematics Education,* 16, 106–119, 1985.

- Sowder, J. "Estimation and Number Sense." In *Handbook of Research on Mathematics Teaching and Learning,* Douglas A. Grouws (ed.). Macmillan Publishing Company, New York, 1992.

Assessment Indicators

- Can students follow the order of operations?
- Can students mentally multiply numbers with ending zeros?
- Can students multiply 2-digit by 1-digit numbers using paper and pencil?
- Can students estimate sums, differences, and products?
- Can students solve problems involving multiplication?
- Can students solve open-response problems and communicate solution strategies?
- Do students demonstrate fluency with the last six multiplication facts (4×6, 4×7, 4×8, 6×7, 6×8, 7×8)?
- Can students write the four number sentences for each of the fact families for the last six facts?

OBSERVATIONAL ASSESSMENT RECORD

(A1) Can students follow the order of operations?

(A2) Can students mentally multiply numbers with ending zeros?

(A3) Can students multiply 2-digit by 1-digit numbers using paper and pencil?

(A4) Can students estimate sums, differences, and products?

(A5) Can students solve problems involving multiplication?

(A6) Can students solve open-response problems and communicate solution strategies?

(A7) Do students demonstrate fluency with the last six multiplication facts (4×6, 4×7, 4×8, 6×7, 6×8, 7×8)?

(A8) Can students write the four number sentences for each of the fact families for the last six facts?

(A9) _____

Name	A1	A2	A3	A4	A5	A6	A7	A8	A9	Comments
1.										
2.										
3.										
4.										
5.										
6.										
7.										
8.										
9.										
10.										
11.										
12.										
13.										

Name	A1	A2	A3	A4	A5	A6	A7	A8	A9	Comments
14.										
15.										
16.										
17.										
18.										
19.										
20.										
21.										
22.										
23.										
24.										
25.										
26.										
27.										
28.										
29.										
30.										
31.										
32.										

Daily Practice and Problems

Patterns in Multiplication

Two Daily Practice and Problems (DPP) items are included for each class session listed in the Unit Outline. The first item is always a Bit and the second is either a Task or a Challenge. Refer to the Daily Practice and Problems and Home Practice Guide in the *Teacher Implementation Guide* for further information on the DPP. A Scope and Sequence Chart for the DPP can be found in the Scope and Sequence Chart & the NCTM *Principles and Standards* section of the *Teacher Implementation Guide*.

A DPP Menu for Unit 7

Eight icons designate the subject matter of the DPP items. Each DPP item falls into one or more of the categories listed below. A brief menu of the DPP items included in Unit 7 follows.

N Number Sense	**Computation**	**Time**	**Geometry**
D, F, H, I, K, L, N–Q, S–X, CC, DD	G, H, S, U–X, Z, CC	C	BB
Math Facts	**$ Money**	**Measurement**	**Data**
A, B, E–H, J, M–O, Y, AA	R, X	L, BB	K, U

The Multiplication and Division Facts

By the end of fourth grade, students in *Math Trailblazers* are expected to demonstrate fluency with all the multiplication and division facts. The DPP for this unit continues the systematic, strategies-based approach to practicing the multiplication facts and learning the division facts through the use of fact families and other strategies. This unit focuses on the last group of facts, known as the last six facts (4 × 6, 4 × 7, 4 × 8, 6 × 7, 6 × 8, and 7 × 8).

The *Triangle Flash Cards: Last Six Facts* follow the Home Practice for this unit in the *Discovery Assignment Book*. Students use the flash cards to practice the multiplication facts through Unit 8. In Units 8 through 16, students use the *Triangle Flash Cards* to practice the division facts. Bit A of the DPP of Unit 7 contains instructions for using the *Triangle Flash Cards* and the *Multiplication Facts I Know* chart. DPP Bit AA is a quiz on the last six multiplication facts.

For more information about the distribution and assessment of the math facts, see the TIMS Tutor: *Math Facts* in the *Teacher Implementation Guide*, the *Grade 4 Facts Resource Guide*, and the DPP guide in the *Unit Resource Guide* for Unit 3.

Students may solve the items individually, in groups, or as a class. The items may also be assigned for homework.

Student Questions	Teacher Notes

 A *Triangle Flash Cards:* **Last Six Facts**

With a partner, use your *Triangle Flash Cards* to quiz each other on the multiplication facts for the last six facts. One partner covers the shaded corner containing the highest number. The second person multiplies the two uncovered numbers. These two are the factors.

Separate the used cards into three piles: those facts you know and can answer quickly, those that you can figure out with a strategy, and those that you need to learn. Practice the last two piles again and then make a list of the facts you need to practice at home for homework.

Circle the facts you know quickly on your *Multiplication Facts I Know* chart.

TIMS Bit

The *Triangle Flash Cards* follow the Home Practice for this unit in the *Discovery Assignment Book*. Part 1 of the Home Practice reminds students to bring home the list of facts they need to practice for homework. The *Triangle Flash Cards* should also be sent home.

Have students record the facts they know well on their *Multiplication Facts I Know* charts. Students should circle the facts they know and can answer quickly. Since these charts can also be used as multiplication tables, students should have them available to use as needed.

Inform students when the quiz on the last six facts will be given. This quiz appears in TIMS Bit AA.

Student Questions	Teacher Notes

 Fact Families for × and ÷

TIMS Task

Complete the number sentences for the related facts.

A. $4 \times 7 =$ ___

___ $\div 4 =$ ___

___ $\div 7 =$ ___

___ $\times 4 =$ ___

B. $8 \times 6 =$ ___

___ $\div 8 =$ ___

___ $\div 6 =$ ___

$6 \times$ ___ $=$ ___

C. $6 \times 7 =$ ___

___ $\div 6 =$ ___

___ $\div 7 =$ ___

___ $\times 6 =$ ___

D. $24 \div 6 =$ ___

___ $\times 6 =$ ___

$24 \div$ ___ $=$ ___

___ $\times 4 =$ ___

E. $8 \times 7 =$ ___

___ $\div 8 =$ ___

___ $\div 7 =$ ___

___ $\times 8 =$ ___

F. $32 \div 8 =$ ___

$4 \times$ ___ $=$ ___

___ $\div 4 =$ ___

___ $\times 4 =$ ___

A. 28; $28 \div 4 = 7$
$28 \div 7 = 4$
$7 \times 4 = 28$

B. 48; $48 \div 8 = 6$
$48 \div 6 = 8$
$6 \times 8 = 48$

C. 42; $42 \div 6 = 7$
$42 \div 7 = 6$
$7 \times 6 = 42$

D. 4; $4 \times 6 = 24$
$24 \div 4 = 6$
$6 \times 4 = 24$

E. 56; $56 \div 8 = 7$
$56 \div 7 = 8$
$7 \times 8 = 56$

F. 4; $4 \times 8 = 32$
$32 \div 4 = 8$
$8 \times 4 = 32$

C **Counting the Time**

TIMS Bit

1. Skip count by 15 minutes from 4:00 to 6:00. Begin this way: 4:00, 4:15, 4:30 . . .

2. Skip count by 20 minutes from 10:00 to 1:00.

3. How much time has gone by from 6:15 to 7:45?

4. How much time has gone by from 3:20 to 4:40?

1. 4:00, 4:15, 4:30, 4:45, 5:00, 5:15, 5:30, 5:45, 6:00

2. 10:00, 10:20, 10:40, 11:00, 11:20, 11:40, 12:00, 12:20, 12:40, 1:00

3. $1\frac{1}{2}$ hours

4. 1 hour 20 minutes

Student Questions	Teacher Notes

D Play *Draw, Place, and Read*

Play the game *Draw, Place, and Read.* You will need 10 cards numbered 0–9. Record 7 blanks on a sheet of paper as shown below.

___ , ___ ___ ___ , ___ ___ ___

1. A caller draws 7 numbers.
2. After each draw, players record the digit drawn in any of the seven places. Once a digit is recorded, it cannot be moved.
3. After all seven draws, the person who makes and reads the highest number earns a point.

TIMS Task N

Students were introduced to the game in Unit 6 Lesson 3. You may distribute copies of the ***Place Value Chart II*** Transparency Master in the ***Unit Resource Guide*** for Unit 6 Lesson 3 for students to record their numbers. Decide ahead of time if you will replace each number after it has been recorded or if you will use each number only once.

E Doubles

1. A. $2 \times 6 =$

   B. $12 + 12 =$

   C. $4 \times 6 =$

2. A. $2 \times 7 =$

   B. $14 + 14 =$

   C. $4 \times 7 =$

3. A. $2 \times 8 =$

   B. $16 + 16 =$

   C. $4 \times 8 =$

What patterns do you see? Describe a strategy for multiplying a number by 4.

TIMS Bit $\frac{5}{\times 7}$

1. A. 12

   B. 24

   C. 24

2. A. 14

   B. 28

   C. 28

3. A. 16

   B. 32

   C. 32

One strategy for multiplying a number by 4 is to multiply first by 2. Then, double the answer. These problems are designed to help students see this pattern. Ask students if they have other patterns for finding the answers to these fact problems.

Break Apart Sevens

  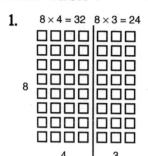

One way to solve 8×7 is to break the 7 into $5 + 2$.

$8 \times 5 = 40$ $8 \times 2 = 16$

8

5   2

$8 \times 7 = 40 + 16 = 56$

$8 \times 5 = 40$ and $8 \times 2 = 16$,
so $8 \times 7 = 40 + 16 = 56$

1. Draw a picture for 8×7 that uses 7 broken into $4 + 3$. Write a number sentence that goes with your picture.

2. Find another way to break up 7. Draw a picture. Write a number sentence for this picture.

3. Write the four number sentences in the fact family for 8×7.

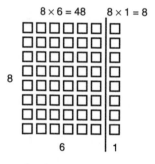

1. $8 \times 4 = 32$ $8 \times 3 = 24$

8

4   3

$8 \times 7 = 32 + 24 = 56$

2. Another way to break up 7 is to use $6 + 1$.

$8 \times 6 = 48$ $8 \times 1 = 8$

8

6   1

$8 \times 7 = 48 + 8 = 56$

3. $8 \times 7 = 56$
   $7 \times 8 = 56$
   $56 \div 8 = 7$
   $56 \div 7 = 8$

Order of Operations

Remember the order of operations as you do the following problems. Do these problems mentally or with pencil and paper, not calculators.

A. $3 \times 5 + 5 =$ B. $6 + 20 \div 4 =$

C. $9 + 8 \times 6 =$ D. $6 \div 2 + 7 \times 6 =$

E. $4 \times 8 + 1 \times 2 =$

F. $10 - 3 \times 3 =$

TIMS Bit

A. $15 + 5 = 20$

B. $6 + 5 = 11$

C. $9 + 48 = 57$

D. $3 + 42 = 45$

E. $32 + 2 = 34$

F. $10 - 9 = 1$

 Operation Target: 1, 3, 6, 9

Play *Operation Target.*

- Use the four digits 1, 3, 6, 9, and the four operations ($+$, $-$, $\times$, $\div$) to make as many numbers as you can.

- In each number sentence, you must use each of the four digits exactly once.

- Use any operation more than once or not at all.

- You can make 2-digit numbers by putting two digits together.

- No fractions or decimals are allowed.

For example: $1 + 63 \div 9 = 8$

1. What is the largest number you can make?

2. What is the smallest number you can make?

3. Make the numbers 1 to 10.

TIMS Challenge

1. $91 \times 63 = 5733$

2. $9 \times 1 - 6 - 3 = 0$

3. Answers will vary.
   $1 = 9 - 6 - 3 + 1$
   $2 = 6 \times 3 \div 9 \times 1$
   $3 = 6 \times 3 \div 9 + 1$
   $4 = 36 \div 9 \times 1$
   $5 = 36 \div 9 + 1$
   $6 = 9 - 6 \div 3 - 1$
   $7 = 9 - 6 \div 3 \times 1$
   $8 = 9 - 6 \div 3 + 1$
   $9 = 9 \div 3 \div 1 + 6$
   $10 = 6 \times 3 - 9 + 1$

Student Questions	Teacher Notes

 Divisible by 2, 3, or 6?

TIMS Bit

1. Which of the following numbers are divisible by 2?

762   1025   8031   4296   1111

2. Which are multiples of 3?

3. Which numbers have 6 as a factor?

Students may use their calculators to check their predictions. In Lesson 2, students discussed divisibility rules for 2, 3, and 6.

1. The even numbers 762 and 4296.

2. 762; 8031; 4296; The sum of the digits of these numbers is a multiple of 3 (e.g., 7 + 6 + 2 = 15 and 8 + 3 + 1 = 12).

3. 762; 4296; These two numbers are multiples of 2 and multiples of 3.

 Story Solving

TIMS Task

Write a story for 6 × 8. Draw a picture for your story and label it with a number sentence.

Students' stories will vary.

 Finding Medians

TIMS Bit

Here is Jackie's data for a paper towel experiment. She dropped water on one sheet of three different brands of paper towels (Ecotowel, Cheap-O, and Handy). She dropped three drops of water on each towel. The water spread out and made a spot. Jackie then measured the area of each spot of water in square centimeters.

This is a review for finding the median value of three trials in an experiment.

Towel Type	Median
Ecotowel	21 sq cm
Cheap-O	37 sq cm
Handy	11 sq cm

T Type of Towel	*A* Area (in sq cm)			
	Trial 1	Trial 2	Trial 3	Median
Ecotowel	23 sq cm	20 sq cm	21 sq cm	
Cheap-O	37 sq cm	36 sq cm	41 sq cm	
Handy	11 sq cm	10 sq cm	12 sq cm	

Find the median area for each type of towel.

Student Questions	Teacher Notes

 Estimating Length

1. Estimate the length and width of your classroom in centimeters. Write down your estimates and be ready to share your estimation strategy with the class.

2. After everyone has made his or her estimate, the class will measure the length and width of the room.

3. Find 10% of the actual length. Is your estimate within 10% of the length? Show how you know.

TIMS Task

This item provides practice estimating length. Be sure to show students a meterstick (100 cm) as a reference number for estimating length.

Assign Question 3 only if students completed Unit 6 Lesson 5 *Close Enough*.

 More Doubles

1. A. $3 \times 7 =$

   B. $21 + 21 =$

   C. $6 \times 7 =$

2. A. $3 \times 8 =$

   B. $24 + 24 =$

   C. $6 \times 8 =$

3. A. $3 \times 4 =$

   B. $12 + 12 =$

   C. $6 \times 4 =$

What patterns do you see? Describe a strategy for multiplying a number by 6.

TIMS Bit

1. A. 21
   B. 42
   C. 42
2. A. 24
   B. 48
   C. 48
3. A. 12
   B. 24
   C. 24

One strategy for multiplying a number by 6 is to multiply first by 3. Then, double the answer. These problems are designed to help students see this pattern. Ask students if they have other patterns for finding the answers to these fact problems.

Student Questions	Teacher Notes

 Break Apart Eights

One way to solve 6×8 is to break the 8 into $5 + 3$.

$6 \times 5 = 30 \qquad 6 \times 3 = 18$

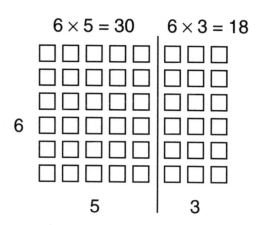

$$6 \times 8 = 30 + 18 = 48$$

$6 \times 5 = 30$ and $6 \times 3 = 18$, so
$6 \times 8 = 30 + 18 = 48$

1. Draw a picture for 6×8 that uses 8 broken into $7 + 1$.

2. Find another way to break up 8. Draw a picture. Write a number sentence for this picture.

3. Write the four number sentences in the fact family for 6×8.

TIMS Task

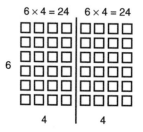

1.
$6 \times 7 = 42 \qquad 6 \times 1 = 6$

$6 \times 8 = 42 + 6 = 48$

2. **Another way to break up 8 is to use $4 + 4$.**

$6 \times 4 = 24 \qquad 6 \times 4 = 24$

$6 \times 8 = 24 + 24 = 48$

3. $6 \times 8 = 48$
   $8 \times 6 = 48$
   $48 \div 6 = 8$
   $48 \div 8 = 6$

 Multiplying by 10

Do these problems in your head.

A. $7 \times 80 =$ B. $6 \times 400 =$

C. $8000 \times 6 =$ D. $700 \times 4 =$

E. $n \times 60 = 420$ F. $800 \times n = 3200$

G. $10 \times 700 =$ H. $0 \times 600 =$

TIMS Bit

In Lesson 4, students discuss patterns in multiplying numbers by multiples of 10.

A. 560   B. 2400

C. 48,000   D. 2800

E. 7   F. 4

G. 7000   H. 0

P Basketball Teams

The local park district sponsors a basketball league. The coaches divide the children into three divisions of equal size. Individual teams are made up of five children. The winning team goes to the state finals. If the league must have more than 100 children, but less than 150, what number of children can form three divisions with teams of five members in each division?

TIMS Challenge   N

The number of children must be a multiple of 15. 105, 120, and 135 are multiples of 15 and within the range of 100 and 150. Encourage students to share their strategies. One partner might skip count by 3s on a calculator while the other skip counts by 5s. Once they get near 100, they can start comparing the numbers in their windows. 105 is the first number greater than 100 that is a multiple of both 3 and 5. Other students may use the divisibility rules they learned in Lesson 2. You can tell 105 is divisible by 3 because the sum of its digits is a multiple of 3. It also is divisible by 5 because its ones' digit is 5.

Q Division by 10

You may use a calculator to divide.

A. $20 \div 10 =$ B. $70 \div 10 =$

C. $100 \div 10 =$ D. $50 \div 10 =$

E. $120 \div 10 =$ F. $180 \div 10 =$

What pattern do you see? How can this pattern help you estimate the answers to the following problems?

$136 \div 10 =$ $178 \div 10 =$ $235 \div 10 =$

TIMS Bit

A. 2

B. 7

C. 10

D. 5

E. 12

F. 18

In the optional lesson, Unit 6 Lesson 5 *Close Enough*, students learn to find 10% of a number. Finding 10% is the same as dividing by 10. Some students may recognize that to approximate 10%, you can truncate the digit in the ones' place. For example, a good approximation for $136 \div 10$ is 13 or 14.

13 or 14; about 18; between 23 and 24

|

 Seventeen Cents

If you have three nickels and two pennies, then you have 17¢. You can show this by writing: $3 \times 5¢ + 2 \times 1¢ = 17¢$.

1. Find all the different combinations of coins that make 17¢. You may use pennies, nickels, and dimes.

2. Write number sentences to show coins that make 17¢.

3. Explain how you know you found all the combinations.

TIMS Challenge

1.

Dimes	Nickels	Pennies
0	0	17
0	1	12
0	2	7
0	3	2
1	0	7
1	1	2

2. An example is:
$1 \times 10¢ + 1 \times 5¢ + 2 \times 1¢ = 17¢$

3. You can be sure you listed all possibilities when you organize your information in a table as shown above.

 Multiplication Times Two

Solve the problems two ways. Use both paper and pencil and mental math. Be prepared to explain your mental math strategies.

1. 79×3

2. 52×6

TIMS Bit

1. 237; A possible mental math strategy: $80 \times 3 - 1 \times 3 = 240 - 3 = 237$.

2. 312; A possible mental math strategy: $50 \times 6 + 2 \times 6 = 300 + 12 = 312$.

Big Numbers

Draw the number line below.

400,000   500,000

1. Make a mark on the line to show 478,923.

2. Round 478,923 to the nearest 100,000.

3. Round 478,923 to the nearest 10,000. What benchmarks did you use? Add these benchmarks to the number line.

4. Round 323,701 to the nearest 100,000. Draw a number line that includes this number and label the number line with benchmarks. Make a mark for 323,701.

5. Round 323,701 to the nearest 10,000. What benchmarks did you use? Add these benchmarks to your number line.

TIMS Task

In Unit 6 Lesson 6, students used number lines to find convenient numbers expressed to the nearest 1000, 10,000, and 100,000. Ask students to sketch their number lines for Question 4 on a transparency or on the chalkboard.

1.–3. 500,000; 480,000

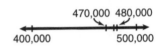

470,000 480,000

400,000   500,000

4.–5. 300,000; 320,000

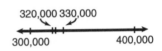

320,000 330,000

300,000   400,000

Student Questions	Teacher Notes

 Finding Means

Here is Jackie's data for a paper towel experiment. She dropped water on one sheet of three different brands of paper towels. She dropped three drops of water on each towel. The water spread out and made a spot. Jackie measured the area of each spot in square centimeters.

T Type of Towel	A Area (in sq cm)			
	Trial 1	Trial 2	Trial 3	Mean
Ecotowel	23 sq cm	20 sq cm	21 sq cm	
Cheap-O	37 sq cm	36 sq cm	41 sq cm	
Handy	11 sq cm	10 sq cm	12 sq cm	

Use a calculator to find the mean area for each type of towel. Give your answer to the nearest cm.

 Adding and Subtracting for Practice

Do the following problems mentally. Be ready to explain how you solved each problem without paper and pencil.

A. 89,300
   − 102

B. 77,900
   + 1100

C. 65,800
   − 5099

Use paper and pencil to solve problems D–F. Use estimation to help you decide if your answers make sense.

D. 13,457
   − 4294

E. 85,609
   − 6725

F. 67,890
   + 32,484

TIMS Bit

This item provides practice for finding the mean value of three trials. Students will use this skill in many labs.

Towel Type	Mean
Ecotowel	21 sq cm
Cheap-O	38 sq cm
Handy	11 sq cm

TIMS Task

Subtracting across zeros using the traditional algorithm is often inefficient. Students can use counting up and counting back strategies to solve A–C. For example, to solve C, they can subtract 100 from 65,800 to get 65,700; add back one to get 65,701; then subtract 5000 to get 60,701.

A. 89,198

B. 79,000

C. 60,701

D. 9163

E. 78,884

F. 100,374

Student Questions	Teacher Notes

 Oceans

1. The Pacific Ocean covers 64,186,300 square miles. The Atlantic Ocean covers 33,420,000 square miles. About how many more square miles does the Pacific Ocean cover than the Atlantic?

2. The Indian Ocean covers 28,350,000 square miles. Do the Atlantic and Indian Oceans combined cover more or less area than the Pacific Ocean?

TIMS Bit

1. About 30,000,000 miles. Round both numbers to the nearest million.
60,000,000 − 30,000,000 = 30,000,000 miles.

2. Less. Round both numbers to the nearest 100,000.
28,000,000 + 33,000,000 = 61,000,000.

 Savings

On Monday, the balance in Nicholas's checking account was $10.

1. On Tuesday, he wrote a check for $25. What was his new balance?

2. On Wednesday, he deposited $50. What was his new balance?

3. On Thursday, he wrote two checks for $20 each. What was his new balance?

4. On Friday, he deposited $25. What was his new balance?

TIMS Challenge

Use this item with students who have completed the optional lesson Unit 3 Lesson 6 *What's Below Zero?*

1. Negative balance of $15
2. $35
3. Negative balance of $5
4. $20

Multiplying by Multiples of 10

A. $600 \times 4 =$
B. $8000 \times 7 =$
C. $4 \times 70 =$
D. $800 \times 6 =$
E. $8 \times 4000 =$
F. $600 \times 7 =$

TIMS Bit

A. 2400 B. 56,000
C. 280   D. 4800
E. 32,000 F. 4200

Multiplication

Use paper and pencil or mental math to solve the following problems. Estimate to see if your answers are reasonable.

1. A. $43 \times 7 =$

   B. $85 \times 7 =$

   C. $62 \times 8 =$

   D. $67 \times 6 =$

   E. $96 \times 4 =$

   F. $79 \times 5 =$

2. Solve Question 1F a different way. Describe both strategies.

TIMS Task

1. A. 301
   B. 595
   C. 496
   D. 402
   E. 384
   F. 395

2. Students can use paper and pencil or mental math to multiply 79×5. Using mental math: $80 \times 5 = 400$ and $400 - (5 \times 1) = 395$.

 **Multiplication Quiz: Last Six Facts**

A. $8 \times 6 =$

B. $6 \times 4 =$

C. $4 \times 7 =$

D. $7 \times 8 =$

E. $6 \times 7 =$

F. $8 \times 4 =$

TIMS Bit

This quiz is on the fifth and final group of multiplication facts, the last six facts. We recommend 1 minute for this quiz. You might want to allow students to change pens after the time is up and complete the remaining problems in a different color.

After students take the test, have them update their *Multiplication Facts I Know* charts.

BB Area and Perimeter

1. What is the area of the shape below?

2. What is the perimeter?

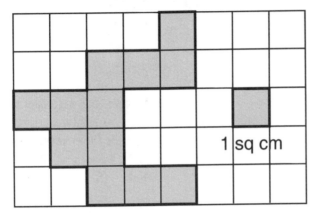

1 sq cm

3. Draw a shape on *Centimeter Grid Paper* that has twice the area of the shape above. What is the perimeter of your shape?

TIMS Task

1. 12 sq cm

2. 24 cm

3. Answers will vary. Two examples of shapes with an area of 24 sq cm are: Perimeter = 28 cm

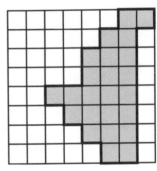

Perimeter = 20 cm

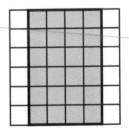

CC More Multiplication

Use paper and pencil or mental math to solve the following problems. Estimate to be sure your answer is reasonable.

1. A. 47 × 9

   B. 64 × 8

2. Explain your estimation strategy for Question 1B.

TIMS Bit

1. A. 423

   B. 512

2. A possible estimation strategy: 60 × 8 = 480 and 70 × 8 = 560, so the product is more than 480, but less than 560.

DD **Within 10%: Area**

Shannon is getting new carpet in her room. She estimated that her bedroom floor has an area of 120 square feet. When she measured her room, she found that the area is 130 square feet.

1. Is her estimate within 10% of the actual area?

2. Is her estimate of 120 square feet a good one for ordering carpet? Why or why not?

TIMS Challenge

Use this Challenge item with students who have completed Lesson 5 *Close Enough* in Unit 6.

1. Yes

2. No, since her estimate was low, even though it was within 10% of the actual area, she wouldn't order enough carpet to cover the floor.

Daily Practice and Problems:
Bit for Lesson 1

A. *Triangle Flash Cards:*
   Last Six Facts (URG p. 10)

With a partner, use your *Triangle Flash Cards* to quiz each other on the multiplication facts for the last six facts. One partner covers the shaded corner containing the highest number. The second person multiplies the two uncovered numbers. These two are the factors.

Separate the used cards into three piles: those facts you know and can answer quickly, those that you can figure out with a strategy, and those that you need to learn. Practice the last two piles again and then make a list of the facts you need to practice at home for homework.

Circle the facts you know quickly on your *Multiplication Facts I Know* chart.

DPP Task is on page 31. Suggestions for using the DPPs are on page 31.

Order of Operations

Estimated
Class
Sessions:
1–2

Students learn about adding, subtracting, multiplying, and dividing using the conventional order of operations. A game, *Operation Target,* provides practice with this order and with basic math facts.

Key Content

• Following the conventional order of operations.

Key Vocabulary

   operation
   order of operations

Materials List

Print Materials for Students

		Math Facts and Daily Practice and Problems	Activity	Homework
Student Books	**Student Guide**		*Order of Operations* Pages 180–183	
	Discovery Assignment Book			Home Practice Parts 1 & 2 Page 85 and *Triangle Flash Cards: Last Six Facts* Page 89
Teacher Resources	**Facts Resource Guide**	DPP Items 7A & 7B Use *Triangle Flash Cards: Last Six Facts* to review the multiplication facts for the last six facts.		
	Unit Resource Guide	DPP Items A–B Pages 10–11		
	Generic Section		*Digit Cards 0–9,* 1–2 per student group and *Operation Cards,* 1 per student group	

available on Teacher Resource CD

All Transparency Masters, Blackline Masters, and Assessment Blackline Masters in the Unit Resource Guide are on the Teacher Resource CD.

Supplies for Each Student

calculator
scissors
envelope for storing flash cards

Materials for the Teacher

2 calculators, one that follows the order of operations and one that does not

Order of Operations

An operation is work that someone or something does. When a surgeon takes out an appendix, he or she performs an *operation*. People who use cranes and bulldozers *operate* heavy machinery. If a pop machine is broken, then we say it is not *operating*.

Things that are done to numbers are also called **operations**. The four basic operations are addition, subtraction, multiplication, and division. People have agreed on a certain **order of operations** for arithmetic problems. The order in which you perform operations in an arithmetic problem is very important. You can see why in the problem below.

Mrs. Dewey brought raisins to the class picnic. There are six boxes of raisins in each snackpack.

180 SG · Grade 4 · Unit 7 · Lesson 1   Order of Operations

Student Guide - Page 180

After the picnic was over, there were 3 individual boxes of raisins and two unopened snackpacks left over. How many boxes of raisins were left?

Jessie said that there were 3 boxes and 2 snackpacks left over. She wrote this number sentence: $3 + 2 \times 6$. But, she didn't know whether to multiply or add first. Try both ways.

If you add $3 + 2$ first, the answer is 30 boxes of raisins. If you multiply 2×6 first, the answer is 15 boxes of raisins. Which is the correct answer?

There were three boxes and two snackpacks of raisins left over. This amount is shown below.

$3 + 2 \times 6 = 15$

If you count up all the boxes, you will see that the correct answer is 15 boxes of raisins left over. So, you need to multiply first in the problem: $3 + 2 \times 6$.

You cannot simply work from left to right when you solve problems like $3 + 2 \times 6$. Mathematicians have agreed on the following rules for the order of operations: First, do all the multiplications and divisions. If there are several multiplications and divisions, solve them from left to right.

When you finish all the multiplying and dividing, then do the additions and subtractions. Work from left to right. Some examples are shown below.

Do the multiplication first. Then, add.

$7 + \underbrace{3 \times 4}_{} = ?$
$7 + \;\; 12 \;\; = 19$

Do the division and multiplication first. Then, add.

$\underbrace{6 \div 2}_{} + \underbrace{8 \times 2}_{} = ?$
$\;\; 3 \;\; + \;\; 16 \;\; = 19$

Order of Operations   SG · Grade 4 · Unit 7 · Lesson 1 181

Student Guide - Page 181

Before the Activity

Obtain at least one calculator that does not use the conventional order of operations. You can test whether a calculator follows the order of operations with the following keystrokes: $\boxed{6}\;\boxed{-}\;\boxed{3}\;\boxed{\times}\;\boxed{2}\;\boxed{=}$. If the calculator gives an answer of 0, it uses the conventional order of operations. Calculators that give an answer of 6 do not use the conventional order of operations.

Content Note

Order of Operations. At first glance, an expression such as $5 + 4 \times 3$ is open to various interpretations. One approach takes $5 + 4 \times 3$ to mean, "First add 5 and 4 to get 9, and then multiply by 3 to obtain 27." This simple left-to-right interpretation is the way many four-function calculators evaluate the expression, but it is incorrect, according to mathematical convention accepted the world over.

The standard mathematical meaning of $5 + 4 \times 3$ is, "First multiply 4 times 3 to get 12, and then add 5 and 12 to get 17." This interpretation is based on a convention known as the algebraic order of operations. This convention specifies the order in which operations in mathematical expressions are to be carried out:

- Do all multiplications and divisions from left to right.
- Then, do all additions and subtractions from left to right.

For example, $48 \div 6 - 3 \times 2 = 8 - 6 = 2$.

"My Dear Aunt Sally" is a mnemonic for the algebraic order of operations. The initials remind us to "Multiply and Divide first, and then Add and Subtract." Make sure that students know that multiplication and division have equal rank. Therefore, multiplication only comes before division if it appears first. For example, $36 \div 9 \times 2 = 4 \times 2 = 8$.

Use of parentheses and exponents will also affect the order of operations. The convention is to calculate the exponents and operations inside parentheses first.

Developing the Activity

Part 1. Order of Operations

Use the *Order of Operations* Activity Pages in the *Student Guide* to explain the **order of operations.**

Compare calculators that follow order of operations with those that do not. Hold up two calculators, one that uses the conventional order of operations and one that does not. Do not tell students which is which; they will figure this out. Write a problem on the board such as: $6 - 3 \times 2$. (See below for more suggestions.) Pass out the two calculators to two different students and have them solve this problem on the calculators by entering the following keystrokes: $\boxed{6}\ \boxed{-}\ \boxed{3}\ \boxed{\times}\ \boxed{2}\ \boxed{=}$. Write the solutions the calculators give on the board. Calculators that follow the order of operations will give a solution of 0. Calculators that do not follow the order of operations will give a solution of 6. Discuss why different calculators give different answers for the same problem. (Many simple four-function calculators carry out all operations as they are entered, rather than following the conventional order of operations. More sophisticated calculators have algebraic operating systems built in.)

- 5 + 4 × 3   Correct answer is 17, incorrect answer is 27
- 5 + 3 × 4   Correct answer is 17, incorrect answer is 32
- 4 × 3 + 5   Correct answer is 17, incorrect answer is 32
- 3 × 4 + 5   Correct answer is 17, incorrect answer is 27
- 6 + 6 × 6   Correct answer is 42, incorrect answer is 72
- 9 − 2 × 3   Correct answer is 3, incorrect answer is 21

Challenge students to determine if the calculators they use in the classroom use the conventional order of operations.

The Calculator Order of Operations section on the *Order of Operations* Activity Pages provides practice with the order of operations and with identifying if calculators follow the order of operations. Students must have calculators for this part. Be sure students predict what a calculator that uses the order of operations will show before they solve each problem.

If the class does not have access to calculators that use the conventional order of operations, discuss possible keystrokes for finding correct answers. For example, one set of possible keystrokes for 3 + 2 × 6 is: $\boxed{2}\ \boxed{\times}\ \boxed{6}\ \boxed{+}\ \boxed{3}\ \boxed{=}$. Possible keystrokes for 48 ÷ 6 − 3 × 2 are: $\boxed{48}\ \boxed{\div}\ \boxed{6}\ \boxed{=}\ \boxed{-}\ \boxed{6}\ \boxed{=}$. (Do 3 × 2 in your head.)

Calculator Order of Operations

For each of these problems, first find the answer. Then, if possible, check your answer using a calculator that follows the order of operations.

1. 4 − 2 + 1	2. 15 − 8 + 6 − 4	3. 4 + 3 × 2
4. 4 + 9 − 3 × 2	5. 5 × 2 + 3	6. 3 + 5 × 2
7. 5 + 2 × 3	8. 6 ÷ 3 × 2	9. 4 × 4 − 4 ÷ 4
10. 4 + 4 × 4 − 4	11. 4 × 4 − 4 − 4	12. 4 × 4 ÷ 4 − 4
13. 10 + 6 × 8	14. 10 − 24 ÷ 6	15. 8 × 7 − 6

Student Guide - Page 182

📓 Journal Prompt

Suppose you have a calculator but you don't know whether it uses the correct order of operations. Explain how you can find out. Be specific.

16. Use 9, 5, 2, and 1 and +, −, ×, and ÷ to make as many whole numbers as you can. For example, 9 + 5 × 2 − 1 = 18. List the numbers you make and show how you made them.

   A. What is the largest whole number you can make?
   B. What is the smallest whole number you can make?
   C. How many whole numbers less than 10 can you make? Write number sentences for each number.
   D. What whole numbers can you make in more than one way? Show at least two number sentences for each.

17. Pick four different digits. Make as many whole numbers as you can using your four new digits and +, −, ×, and ÷. List the numbers you make and show how you made them.

18. Nila used 1, 2, 3, and 4 to make 10. How do you think she did it? Can you think of another way?

19. Luis used 1, 2, 3, and 4 to make 24. How could he have done it?

20. Romesh used 1, 3, 5, and 7 to make 8. How could he have done it?

21. Make up your own problem like Questions 18, 19, and 20.

Order of Operations   SG · Grade 4 · Unit 7 · Lesson 1 183

Student Guide - Page 183

Part 2. *Operation Target*

Operation Target, located in the *Student Guide,* is a game that provides practice with the order of operations. Students use four digits and the four arithmetic operations (+, −, ×, ÷) to generate as many different whole numbers as possible. Students should perform or check their computations with a calculator that uses the conventional order of operations.

Quite a few different numbers can be made using 9, 5, 2, and 1. For example:

$$9 + 5 + 2 + 1 = 17$$
$$9 - 5 - 2 - 1 = 1$$
$$1 \times 2 \times 9 \times 5 = 90$$
$$5 \times 2 + 1 + 9 = 20$$
$$2 \times 5 \div 1 + 9 = 19$$
$$2 \times 1 + 9 \times 5 = 47$$

A restriction to positive whole numbers is explicit in the rules, but may need to be emphasized. Therefore, the smallest number that can be made is 0 ($0 = 5 \times 2 - 9 - 1$). If you allow negative numbers, then the smallest number is $1 - 5 \times 2 \times 9 = $ -89. (But, we suggest not allowing negative numbers at this time. The exclusion of negative numbers applies to their use in the number sentence, i.e., $2 - 5 + 1 + 9$. The first operation, $2 - 5$, results in a negative number. This should not be allowed.) Another restriction that is not explicit is that the use of 2-digit numbers is not allowed. So, for example, $25 \times 91 = 2275$ is not allowed.

Digit Cards 0–9 and *Operation Cards* in the Generic Section are templates for cards that students may find useful when they play the game. The game can be played without cards, but the cards may make it easier for some students. The cards can be arranged and rearranged to form expressions (e.g., $5 + 9 - 2 \div 1$ or $9 - 5 + 2 \div 1$), which can then be evaluated using a calculator that uses the conventional order of operations.

Suggestions for Teaching the Lesson

Math Facts

DPP item A provides multiplication practice with the *Triangle Flash Cards* for the last six facts. DPP Task B presents fact families for the last six facts.

Homework and Practice

- The Calculator Order of Operations section on the *Order of Operations* Activity Pages may be assigned for homework. If students have a calculator at home, ask them to find out if it uses the correct order of operations.

- After students understand the rules, assign *Operation Target* with different numbers for homework.

- Assign Parts 1 and 2 of the Home Practice. Part 1 of the Home Practice reminds students to use the *Triangle Flash Cards* to practice multiplication for the last six facts. Part 2 provides practice following the order of operations.

Answers for Part 2 of the Home Practice can be found in the Answer Key at the end of this lesson and at the end of this unit.

Assessment

One way to assess students is a simple worksheet with problems that require following the order of operations. For example, the following ten expressions can be made into a brief quiz:

$$5 + 4 \times 3$$
$$6 + 8 \div 2$$
$$5 \times 2 - 6 \div 2$$
$$5 + 4 \times 3$$
$$4 \times 4 - 4 \div 4$$
$$4 + 4 \times 4 - 4$$
$$5 \times 2 + 5 \times 4$$
$$8 \times 3 - 8 \times 3$$
$$2 + 2 \times 2$$
$$6 + 15 \div 3$$

A collection of such problems can also be used for homework.

Daily Practice and Problems: Task for Lesson 1

B. Task: Fact Families for × and ÷

(URG p. 11)

Complete the number sentences for the related facts.

A. $4 \times 7 = \underline{\quad}$
$\underline{\quad} \div 4 = \underline{\quad}$
$\underline{\quad} \div 7 = \underline{\quad}$
$\underline{\quad} \times 4 = \underline{\quad}$

B. $8 \times 6 = \underline{\quad}$
$\underline{\quad} \div 8 = \underline{\quad}$
$\underline{\quad} \div 6 = \underline{\quad}$
$6 \times \underline{\quad} = \underline{\quad}$

C. $6 \times 7 = \underline{\quad}$
$\underline{\quad} \div 6 = \underline{\quad}$
$\underline{\quad} \div 7 = \underline{\quad}$
$\underline{\quad} \times 6 = \underline{\quad}$

D. $24 \div 6 = \underline{\quad}$
$\underline{\quad} \times 6 = \underline{\quad}$
$24 \div \underline{\quad} = \underline{\quad}$
$\underline{\quad} \times 4 = \underline{\quad}$

E. $8 \times 7 = \underline{\quad}$
$\underline{\quad} \div 8 = \underline{\quad}$
$\underline{\quad} \div 7 = \underline{\quad}$
$\underline{\quad} \times 8 = \underline{\quad}$

F. $32 \div 8 = \underline{\quad}$
$4 \times \underline{\quad} = \underline{\quad}$
$\underline{\quad} \div 4 = \underline{\quad}$
$\underline{\quad} \times 4 = \underline{\quad}$

Name _____ Date _____

Unit 7: Home Practice

Part 1 *Triangle Flash Cards: Last Six Facts*

Study for the quiz on the multiplication facts for the last six facts. Take home your *Triangle Flash Cards: Last Six Facts* and your list of facts you need to study.

Here's how to use the flash cards. Ask a family member to choose one flash card at a time. Your partner should cover the corner containing the highest number. This number will be the answer to a multiplication fact. Multiply the two uncovered numbers.

Your teacher will tell you when the quiz on the last six facts will be.

Part 2 Order of Operations

1. Remember the order of operations as you do the following problems. You may use a calculator, but be sure you follow the order of operations even if your calculator does not.

A. $7 \times 2 + 5 = \underline{\quad}$ B. $8 + 4 \times 3 = \underline{\quad}$

C. $7 + 24 \div 3 = \underline{\quad}$ D. $7 \times 4 + 5 \times 2 = \underline{\quad}$

E. $8 \times 6 - 3 \times 3 = \underline{\quad}$ F. $36 \div 9 + 6 \times 7 = \underline{\quad}$

G. $7 + 9 \times 8 - 5 = \underline{\quad}$ H. $100 - 49 \div 7 + 10 = \underline{\quad}$

2. Play *Operation Target*. Use the numbers 1, 2, 3, and 4 and the four operations to make as many different whole numbers as you can. You need paper, a pencil, and a calculator. In each number sentence, you must use each of the four digits exactly once. You can use operations more than once or not at all. For example: To make 10 you could write: $4 \times 1 + 2 \times 3 = 10$. Use a separate sheet of paper to write your number sentences for each of the numbers you make.

Discovery Assignment Book - Page 85

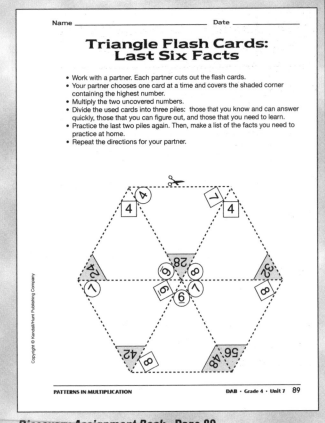

Triangle Flash Cards: Last Six Facts

- Work with a partner. Each partner cuts out the flash cards.
- Your partner chooses one card at a time and covers the shaded corner containing the highest number.
- Multiply the two uncovered numbers.
- Divide the used cards into three piles: those that you know and can answer quickly, those that you can figure out, and those that you need to learn.
- Practice the last two piles again. Then, make a list of the facts you need to practice at home.
- Repeat the directions for your partner.

PATTERNS IN MULTIPLICATION   DAB · Grade 4 · Unit 7   89

Discovery Assignment Book - Page 89

Suggestions for Teaching the Lesson (continued)

Extension

- Ask students to make up problems that a calculator will answer incorrectly if it does not use the conventional order of operations. Also make up problems that such a calculator will get right.

- *Operation Target* variations:

  Variation 1: Play with different digits. For a given set of digits, how many of the whole numbers up to 25 can you make?

  Variation 2: Allow fractions and decimals. Now what numbers can be obtained?

  Variation 3: Allow the use of 2-digit numbers. So, for example, using the digits 9, 5, 2, and 1, the following is permitted: $12 \times 95 = 1140$. Now what is the largest number that can be obtained?

AT A GLANCE

Math Facts and Daily Practice and Problems

DPP items A and B provide practice with the last six facts using flash cards and fact families.

Part 1. Order of Operations

1. Read and discuss the *Order of Operations* Activity Pages in the *Student Guide*.
2. Discuss the conventional order of operations.
3. Use the discrepancy in answers from calculators that do and do not use the conventional order of operations to motivate the lesson.
4. Assign *Questions 1–15* of the Calculator Order of Operations section. Remind students to predict what the calculator window will show before they solve each problem.

Part 2. *Operation Target*

Introduce and play the game *Operation Target*.

Homework

1. Assign *Operation Target* for homework.
2. Assign Parts 1 and 2 in the Home Practice.

Notes:

Student Guide

Questions 1–21 (SG pp. 182–183)

1. 3
2. 9
3. 10
4. 7
5. 13
6. 13
7. 11
8. 4
9. 15
10. 16
11. 8
12. 0
13. 58
14. 6
15. 50
16. **A.** *91; $9 \times 5 \times 2 + 1 = 91$
    B. *0; $5 \times 2 - 9 - 1 = 0$
    C. Answers will vary.
    $0 = 5 \times 2 - 9 - 1$
    $1 = 9 - 5 - 2 - 1$
    $2 = 5 \times 2 - 9 + 1$
    $3 = 9 - 5 - 2 + 1$
    $4 = $ If 2-digit numbers are allowed, $15 - 9 - 2$.
    $5 = 9 + 2 - 5 - 1$
    $6 = 9 - 5 \times 1 + 2$
    $7 = 9 + 1 - 5 + 2$
    $8 = $ If 2-digit numbers are allowed, $15 - 9 + 2$.
    $9 = $ If 2-digit numbers are allowed, $19 - 5 \times 2$.

D. Answers will vary. For example, three number sentences that make 1 are: $1 = 9 - 5 - 2 - 1$ and $1 = 5 \times 2 - 9 \times 1$ and $1 = 2 \times 5 \div 1 - 9$; Here are two number sentences that make 5: $5 = 9 + 2 - 5 - 1$ and $5 = 9 - 1 + 2 - 5$

17. Answers will vary.
18. Answers will vary. Two examples are: $4 \times 3 - 2 \times 1$ and $4 + 3 + 2 + 1$
19. Answers will vary. The numbers in the following sentence can be written in any order: $4 \times 3 \times 2 \times 1$
20. Answers will vary. Two possible solutions are: $5 \times 3 - 7 \times 1$ and $7 + 5 - 3 - 1$.
21. Answers will vary.

Discovery Assignment Book

**Home Practice (DAB p. 85)

Part 2. Order of Operations

Questions 1–2

1. **A.** 19
   B. 20
   C. 15
   D. 38
   E. 39
   F. 46
   G. 74
   H. 103
2. Answers will vary.

*Answers and/or discussion are included in the Lesson Guide.
**Answers for all the Home Practice in the *Discovery Assignment Book* are at the end of the unit.

C. Counting the Time (URG p. 11)

1. Skip count by 15 minutes from 4:00 to 6:00. Begin this way: 4:00, 4:15, 4:30 . . .

2. Skip count by 20 minutes from 10:00 to 1:00.

3. How much time has gone by from 6:15 to 7:45?

4. How much time has gone by from 3:20 to 4:40?

E. Doubles (URG p. 12)

1. A. $2 \times 6 =$

   B. $12 + 12 =$

   C. $4 \times 6 =$

2. A. $2 \times 7 =$

   B. $14 + 14 =$

   C. $4 \times 7 =$

3. A. $2 \times 8 =$

   B. $16 + 16 =$

   C. $4 \times 8 =$

What patterns do you see? Describe a strategy for multiplying a number by 4.

DPP Tasks are on page 41. Suggestions for using the DPPs are on page 41.

LESSON GUIDE 2
Divisibility Rules

Estimated Class Sessions: 2

Students explore ways to determine whether a multidigit number is evenly divisible by 2, 3, 5, 6, 9, or 10. Being able to tell whether a number is divisible by a given number will help students choose convenient numbers in later computations with division.

Key Content

- Identifying and describing patterns in the multiples of 2, 3, 5, 6, 9, and 10.
- Exploring the inverse relationship between multiplication and division.
- Determining whether a number is divisible by 2, 3, 5, 6, 9, or 10.
- Developing number sense.

Key Vocabulary

divisible
factor
multiple
remainder

Materials List

Print Materials for Students

		Math Facts and Daily Practice and Problems	Activity	Homework	Written Assessment
Student Books	Student Guide		*Divisibility Rules* Pages 184–188	*Divisibility Rules* Homework Section Page 189	
	Discovery Assignment Book				Home Practice Part 3 Page 86
Teacher Resources	Facts Resource Guide	DPP Items 7E & 7F			
	Unit Resource Guide	DPP Items C–F Pages 11–13	*100 Chart* Page 44, 2–3 per student		

available on Teacher Resource CD

All Transparency Masters, Blackline Masters, and Assessment Blackline Masters in the Unit Resource Guide are on the Teacher Resource CD.

Supplies for Each Student

blue and red crayons or colored pencils
calculator

Materials for the Teacher

Transparency of *100 Chart* Blackline Master (Unit Resource Guide) Page 44
blue and red overhead markers

Student Guide - Page 184

🅣IMS Tip

Create a bulletin board for the divisibility rules. As students explore multiples of 2, 3, 5, 6, 9, and 10, add rules for identifying each on the board. Students may use the bulletin board as a reference.

Developing the Activity

Part 1. Divisibility by 2 and 3

Read the opening vignette on the *Divisibility Rules* Activity Pages in the *Student Guide*. Shannon, Roberto, and Ming are discussing whether 318 is divisible by 2. Roberto reasons that 318 is divisible by 2 since it is an even number.

Questions 1–4 in the *Student Guide* discuss numbers that are divisible by 2. For **Question 1,** students circle the multiples of 2 in blue on a copy of the *100 Chart* and describe patterns they see. If students are able to identify even numbers and recognize them as being divisible by 2, you may not need to discuss these questions. However, it is worthwhile for students to see the pattern that emerges when the multiples of two are circled on the *100 Chart* (See Figure 1). Using a transparency of the *100 Chart,* circle the multiples of 2 in blue along with your students. Students should see that all multiples of 2, or even numbers, end in 0, 2, 4, 6, or 8. The even numbers form five straight columns on the chart.

1	②	3	④	5	⑥	7	⑧	9	⑩
11	⑫	13	⑭	15	⑯	17	⑱	19	⑳
21	㉒	23	㉔	25	㉖	27	㉘	29	㉚
31	㉜	33	㉞	35	㊱	37	㊳	39	㊵
41	㊷	43	㊹	45	㊻	47	㊽	49	㊿
51	㋒	53	㋔	55	㋖	57	㋘	59	60
61	62	63	64	65	66	67	68	69	70
71	72	73	74	75	76	77	78	79	80
81	82	83	84	85	86	87	88	89	90
91	92	93	94	95	96	97	98	99	100

Figure 1: *Multiples of 2 on the* 100 Chart

Question 2 asks students to extend the pattern they see to larger numbers.

- *In which column would 318 be on an extended chart?*

Since the ones' digit is 8, the number 318 would fall in the same column as the 8, 18, 28, 38, etc. No matter how large a number is, the digit in the ones' place tells us whether the number is even or odd.

Some students may recognize which numbers in *Question 3* are evenly divisible by 2 without a calculator. However, in order to write multiplication and division number sentences, calculators should be made available *(Question 3B)*. If a number is divisible by 2, the answer in the calculator window will be a whole number. When a number is *not* divisible by 2, a whole number does not result. The introduction on the first page of the *Divisibility Rules* Activity Pages clarifies the calculator's decimal answer to 319 ÷ 2.

Have students turn to the Is It Divisible by 3? section in the *Student Guide*. Three pairs of related multiplication and division sentences are listed to show that the numbers 12, 21, and 30 are divisible by 3. Emphasize that a number is divisible by 3 if 3 is one of its factors. Use *Questions 5–11* to guide a discussion about divisibility by 3.

Question 5 asks students to mark a red "X" on all of the multiples of 3. As they are marking the numbers, stop them periodically and ask them to say a multiplication or division sentence for a specific multiple of 3. For example, as a child skip counts by three and marks 18 with a red "X," ask:

- *Can you tell me a multiplication sentence that shows that 3 is a factor of 18? Can you tell me a division sentence that shows me that 18 is divisible by 3? (3 × 6 = 18; 18 ÷ 3 = 6)*

As students look at their completed copies of the *100 Chart,* ask them to concentrate on those numbers marked in red—the multiples of 3. Students may notice that the multiples of three form six diagonals through the *100 Chart.* This is shown in Figure 2. Others may note that some of the numbers they marked red were already circled in blue. (These students are on their way to exploring divisibility by 6. The numbers that are marked in red *and* circled in blue are multiples of 6.) Others may compare the multiples of 3 to the multiples of 2 and say, "These aren't as easy to identify. A multiple of 3 can end in any number. Multiples of 2 only end in 0, 2, 4, 6, or 8."
(Question 6)

TIMS Tip

Later in this lesson, students will explore divisibility of 6 by looking at the multiples of 6, the multiples of 2, and the multiples of 3. Students should keep their copies of the *100 Chart* Blackline Master in a safe place since the same copy will be used throughout the lesson.

---

1. On a copy of the *100 Chart,* use a blue crayon or pencil to circle all the **multiples** of 2. Then, describe any patterns you see. Save your copy of the *100 Chart* for later use.

2. Shannon's book is 318 pages long. In which column would 318 be if the 100 chart kept going beyond 100?

3. A. Which of the following numbers are divisible by 2? Why do you think so? Check your predictions using a calculator.

| 109 | 213 | 216 | 275 | 784 |
| 1000 | 1358 | 2462 | 6767 | 8091 |

   B. Write a multiplication sentence and a division sentence for each number that is divisible by 2. For example: 216 ÷ 2 = 108 and 108 × 2 = 216

4. How can you tell if a number is divisible by 2?

Is It Divisible by 3?

12 is divisible by 3.	21 is divisible by 3.	30 is divisible by 3.
4 × 3 = 12	7 × 3 = 21	10 × 3 = 30
12 ÷ 3 = 4	21 ÷ 3 = 7	30 ÷ 3 = 10

3 is a factor of 12, 21, and 30. A factor of a number can be divided evenly into the number, that is, the answer (or quotient) is a whole number. Since 12, 21, and 30 can be divided by 3 evenly, we say that 12, 21, and 30 are divisible by 3.

5. Use your copy of the *100 Chart* that you used earlier (the multiples of 2 should be circled in blue). Using a red crayon or pencil, mark all the multiples of 3 with an "X." Your *100 Chart* should look like the one below.

1	②	⨉	④	5	⑥̸	7	⑧	⨉	⑩
11	⑫̸	13	⑭	⨉	⑯	17	⑱̸	19	⑳
⨉	㉒	23	㉔	25	㉖	⨉	㉘	29	㉚̸

Divisibility Rules   SG · Grade 4 · Unit 7 · Lesson 2   185

Student Guide - Page 185

Content Note
Divisibility.

$$10 \div 2 = 5 \qquad\qquad 9 \div 2 = 4.5$$
10 is divisible by 2   9 is not divisible by 2

When we say a number is **divisible** by 2, we mean 2 divides the number evenly, that is, the answer is a whole number. The answers to the above problems show that 10 is divisible by 2, but 9 is not.

A number is divisible by 2 if the digit in the ones' place is 0, 2, 4, 6, or 8.

A number is divisible by 3 if the sum of its digits is divisible by 3.

A number is divisible by 5 if the digit in the ones' place is 0 or 5.

A number is divisible by 6 if it is divisible by 2 and divisible by 3.

A number is divisible by 9 if the sum of its digits is divisible by 9.

Furthermore, the process of adding digits can be repeated until nine itself results. 981 is divisible by 9: 9 + 8 + 1 = 18 (18 is divisible by 9). Now add the digits in 18: 1 + 8 = 9.

1	2	~~3~~	4	5	~~6~~	7	8	~~9~~	10
11	~~12~~	13	14	~~15~~	16	17	~~18~~	19	20
~~21~~	22	23	~~24~~	25	26	~~27~~	28	29	~~30~~
31	32	~~33~~	34	35	~~36~~	37	38	~~39~~	40
41	~~42~~	43	44	~~45~~	46	47	~~48~~	49	50
~~51~~	52	53	~~54~~	55	56	~~57~~	58	59	~~60~~
61	62	~~63~~	64	65	~~66~~	67	68	~~69~~	70
71	~~72~~	73	74	~~75~~	76	77	~~78~~	79	80
~~81~~	82	83	~~84~~	85	86	~~87~~	88	89	~~90~~
91	92	~~93~~	94	95	~~96~~	97	98	~~99~~	100

1	(2)	~~3~~	(4)	5	(~~6~~)	7	(8)	~~9~~	(10)
11	(~~12~~)	13	(14)	~~15~~	(16)	17	(~~18~~)	19	(20)
~~21~~	(22)	23	(~~24~~)	25	(26)	~~27~~	(28)	29	(~~30~~)
31	(32)	~~33~~	(34)	35	(~~36~~)	37	(38)	~~39~~	(40)
41	(~~42~~)	43	(44)	~~45~~	(46)	47	(~~48~~)	49	(50)
~~51~~	(52)	53	(~~54~~)	55	(56)	~~57~~	(58)	59	(~~60~~)
61	(62)	~~63~~	(64)	65	(~~66~~)	67	(68)	~~69~~	(70)
71	(~~72~~)	73	(74)	~~75~~	(76)	77	(~~78~~)	79	(80)
~~81~~	(82)	83	(~~84~~)	85	(86)	~~87~~	(88)	89	(~~90~~)
91	(92)	~~93~~	(94)	95	(~~96~~)	97	(98)	~~99~~	(100)

Figure 2: *Multiples of 3 only and multiples of 2 and 3 combined*

0	1	2	~~3~~	4	5	~~6~~	7	8	~~9~~
10	11	~~12~~	13	14	~~15~~	16	17	~~18~~	19
20	~~21~~	22	23	~~24~~	25	26	~~27~~	28	29
~~30~~	31	32	~~33~~	34	35	~~36~~	37	38	~~39~~
40	41	~~42~~	43	44	~~45~~	46	47	~~48~~	49
50	~~51~~	52	53	~~54~~	55	56	~~57~~	58	59
~~60~~	61	62	~~63~~	64	65	~~66~~	67	68	~~69~~
70	71	~~72~~	73	74	~~75~~	76	77	~~78~~	79
80	~~81~~	82	83	~~84~~	85	86	~~87~~	88	89
~~90~~	91	92	~~93~~	94	95	~~96~~	97	98	~~99~~
100									

Figure 4: *Starting with 0 on the 100 Chart*

As students share the patterns they see, a discussion about divisibility by 3 should arise. In **Questions 7–9,** students use their copies of the *100 Chart* and calculators to determine if a number is divisible by 3. These problems also provide further practice in writing related multiplication and division sentences. In **Question 10,** students start to explore numbers greater than 100. Some students may predict that 102 is divisible by 3 since it would fall on the same diagonal as 84 and 93. (See Figure 2.) However, 101 is not divisible by 3 since it would not fall on the diagonal.

Help students focus on the multiples of three by writing the numbers in each diagonal on the chalkboard as shown in Figure 3. When looking at the multiples of 3 this way, students may recognize some of the following patterns:

*   The multiples of 9 appear in the third column.
*   The numbers in each column increase by 9 as you read the numbers from top to bottom.
*   The digits in the tens' place increase by one as you go down the first three columns. The digits in the ones' place decrease by one as you go down each of the first three columns. The remaining columns also decrease by one in the ones' place, but they start with a zero.

3	6	9	30	60	90
12	15	18	39	69	99
21	24	27	48	78	
	33	36	57	87	
	42	45	66	96	
	51	54	75		
		63	84		
		72	93		
		81			

Figure 3: *Multiples of 3*

Students who notice the multiples of 9 listed may begin to ask such questions as, *"Does this mean numbers that can be divided by 9 evenly can also be divided by 3 evenly?"* You may wish to pursue this now or tell students that later they will investigate the multiples of 9. Students may reason that a multiple of 9 or a number divisible by 9 is also divisible by 3 since 3 is a factor of 9.

One or two students may recognize that the digits in the numbers in the first diagonal add up to 3; those in the second diagonal add up to 6; those in the third add up to 9; those in the fourth add up to 12 (except for 30); those in the fifth add up to 15 (except for 60), and the digits in 99 add up to 18. The sum of the digits of a multiple of three is also a multiple of 3. (Note that if we used a 99 chart instead of a 100 chart, as shown in Figure 4, the number 30 would be in the same diagonal as the 3, 12, and 21. 60 would be in the same diagonal as the 42 and 51.) Students may question if this pattern continues. The sum of the digits in 99 is 18. If the sum of the digits of a number is 21, will that number be divisible by 3? Try it! The digits in 2397 produce the sum of 21. You might predict then that 2397 is in fact divisible by 3. Use a calculator and check the prediction.

We suggest that you do not proceed to *Question 11* until students have investigated patterns and shared their thoughts. Some students might recognize the divisibility test for division by 3—a number is divisible by 3 if the sum of its digits is a multiple of 3. When you feel it is appropriate, ask student pairs or groups to describe the pattern Ming recognizes in Mrs. Dewey's data table in *Question 11*. After students have had some time to discuss it, copy the table from *Question 11* onto the board. If a pair of students have recognized the pattern, ask them to come to the board to explain it. If not, list additional multiples of three on the board and the sum of their digits, extending Mrs. Dewey's data table. Ask students what the "sum of the digits" is for each and point out that the sum is a multiple of three (e.g., 198 is a multiple of 3: $1 + 9 + 8 = 18$. 18 is a multiple of 3). Then, provide counterexamples. Ask students to name some numbers that are not divisible by three and test those numbers (e.g., 88 is not a multiple of 3: $8 + 8 = 16$. 16 is not a multiple of 3). The sums of the digits of these numbers are not multiples of 3.

List several numbers on the board and have students use the divisibility rule for 3 to predict whether or not each number is divisible by 3. Have them check each one on a calculator. When students are ready to proceed independently, assign *Questions 12–15* for practice or for homework.

Question 15 asks students whether 12,345,678 is divisible by 2 and 3. Since it is even, it is divisible by 2. Since the sum of the digits is 36, a multiple of 3, it is also divisible by 3.

Part 2. Divisibility by 6 and 9

To explore divisibility by 6, students need their copies of the *100 Chart* from Part 1 of this lesson. The multiples of 2 should be circled in blue. The multiples of 3 should be marked in red.

Question 16A asks students to identify which numbers listed in *Question 14* are divisible by 6. Students should use a calculator to check each number. Some students may notice that the numbers divisible by both 2 *and* 3 (126, 342, and 1002) are also divisible by 6. Then, *Question 16B* asks students to skip count by 6s on their copies of the *100 Chart* in order to look for patterns in the multiples of 6. They should recognize that there is no need to mark the multiples of 6 on the chart because they are already marked with blue circles *and* red Xs. Ask students questions such as:

6. Describe any patterns you see.

7. Use your copy of the *100 Chart* and your calculator to help you answer the following questions:
   A. Is 27 a multiple of 3? Write a multiplication sentence.
   B. Is 27 divisible by 3? Write a division sentence.
   C. Is 51 a multiple of 3? Write a multiplication sentence.
   D. Is 51 divisible by 3? Write a division sentence.

8. A. Is 14 a multiple of 3? How do you know?
   B. If 14 is divided by 3, what is the remainder? Write a multiplication or division sentence. Remember to include the remainder.
   C. Use your calculator. Press: [14] [÷] [3] [=]
      How does your calculator show whether 14 is divisible by 3?

9. Is 74, 75, or 76 divisible by 3? Use your copy of the *100 Chart* or a calculator to decide. Write a division sentence showing which number is divisible by 3.

10. Look carefully at your *100 Chart*. Write in more numbers below it if you need to.
    A. Predict: Is 101 divisible by 3? Check your prediction with a calculator.
    B. Predict: Is 102 divisible by 3? Check your prediction with a calculator.
    C. Predict: Which of the following is divisible by 3? 116, 117, or 118? Why do you think so? Check your prediction with a calculator.

11. Mrs. Dewey started listing numbers from the *100 Chart* that were divisible by 3. Ming saw a pattern. Do you? Explain.

Number	Sum of Digits
18	$1 + 8 = 9$
42	$4 + 2 = 6$
51	$5 + 1 = 6$
84	$8 + 4 = 12$
99	$9 + 9 = 18$

186 SG · Grade 4 · Unit 7 · Lesson 2   **Divisibility Rules**

Student Guide - Page 186

12. Name a number greater than 125 that is divisible by 3. Check your prediction.

13. Name a number greater than 200 that is divisible by 3. Check your prediction.

14. Use the numbers below to make predictions for Questions 14A–14C. Then, check your predictions with a calculator.

| 126 | 209 | 342 | 177 | 1664 |
| 1002 | 991 | 297 | 8770 | 8775 |

   A. Which of the numbers are divisible by 3?
   B. Which are divisible by 2?
   C. Which are divisible by 2 and 3?

15. Is 12,345,678 divisible by 2? Divisible by 3? Check using your calculator.

Is It Divisible by 6?

16. A. Find out which numbers in Question 14 are divisible by 6. Use a calculator.
    B. How can you determine if a number is divisible by 6? Find the multiples of 6 by skip counting by 6s on your *100 Chart*. What do you notice?
    C. Based on the patterns you see, predict whether 12,345,678 (from Question 15) is divisible by 6. Check your prediction.

17. A. Give a number greater than 150 that is divisible by 6.
    B. Give a number greater than 225 that is divisible by 6. Explain how you found your number.

Divisibility Rules   SG · Grade 4 · Unit 7 · Lesson 2 187

Student Guide - Page 187

- *Which numbers in **Question 14** did we find were divisible by 2, 3, and 6? (126, 342, 1002)*
- *Why do you suppose all the multiples of 6 are also multiples of 2 and 3? (6 is the same as 2×3; 3 and 2 are both factors of 6)*

Since a number that is divisible by 6 is one that is also divisible by 2 and 3, students may predict that the number 12,345,678 is divisible by 6. *(Question 15)* Checking this on the calculator will prove them to be correct.

For further practice, write several numbers on the board. Ask:

- *Which numbers are divisible by 6?* (Students might first eliminate all odd numbers. Then, they must identify which of the even numbers are divisible by 3. Once they have done so, they have identified the multiples of 6.)

Question 17 may be assigned as a journal prompt. Asking students to explain how they solved these two problems will give you insight into their understanding of multiples, factors, and divisibility. Some students might choose numbers and play with the digits so that the last digit is a 0, 2, 4, 6, or 8 and that the sum of the digits is a multiple of three. They must also keep in mind that the number chosen should be greater than 150 for *Question 17A* and greater than 225 for *Question 17B.* Other students might choose a number at random, multiply it by 6 and see if the product is greater than 150 *(Question 17A).* These students can solve the problem using trial-and-error.

After students have explored the divisibility rules for 2, 3, and 6, student pairs may complete *Questions 18–22* in the *Student Guide.* These questions explore divisibility by 9. Students completed an activity similar to this in third grade when learning their multiplication facts (Unit 11). They also explored patterns in the multiples of nine while working on the multiplication facts for the nines in Unit 6. (See DPP item C in Unit 6.)

- When the products are listed in a column, as below, it is easy to see that the digits in the tens' place count up by ones (0, 1, 2, 3 . . .) and that the digits in the ones' place count down by ones (9, 8, 7. . .).

9
18
27
36
45
54
63
72
81
90

Is It Divisible by 9?

Explore

18. Copy and complete the list of facts for 9. Then, write the products in a column, one on each line.

$$1 \times 9 =$$
$$2 \times 9 =$$
$$3 \times 9 =$$
$$4 \times 9 =$$
$$5 \times 9 =$$
$$6 \times 9 =$$
$$7 \times 9 =$$
$$8 \times 9 =$$
$$9 \times 9 =$$
$$9 \times 10 =$$

19. What patterns do you see? What can you say about the sum of the digits of the products?

20. Use your calculator to find more multiples of 9. Find the products below.

A. $9 \times 634 =$
B. $9 \times 23 =$
C. $9 \times 37 =$
D. $9 \times 73 =$
E. $9 \times 143 =$
F. $9 \times 444 =$
G. $9 \times 754 =$
H. $9 \times 4421 =$

21. Go back and add the digits of each product in Question 20.
For example: $9 \times 634 = 5706$
Add the digits in 5706: $5 + 7 + 0 + 6 = 18$
Now, add the digits in 18: $1 + 8 = 9$
Describe what happens when you add the digits of a multiple of 9.

22. A. Predict which numbers below are divisible by 9. Show how you decided.
B. Then, check using a calculator.
C. Finally, write a multiplication and division sentence for each multiple of 9 you identify.

| 172 | 144 | 743 | 747 | 1007 |
| 2556 | 4906 | 8721 | 9908 | 12,987 |

188 SG · Grade 4 · Unit 7 · Lesson 2   **Divisibility Rules**

Student Guide - Page 188

- The sum of the two digits in each of the products listed above is 9. In fact, the sum of the digits of any multiple of 9 is also a multiple of 9.

The process of adding digits can be repeated until nine itself results. This is illustrated in **Question 21.** $9 \times 634 = 5706$. Adding the product's digits provides a multiple of 9: $5 + 7 + 0 + 6 = 18$. Adding the digits of this sum results in 9: $1 + 8 = 9$.

Have students work with other multiples of 9 in **Questions 20–21** to discover that this pattern is consistent. In **Question 22,** students may use this pattern to predict whether a number is a multiple of 9. This will be a useful way to check answers once students learn paper-and-pencil methods for multiplying multidigit numbers (Lesson 5). To check the answer to 1569×9, for example, you can add the digits of the product to determine whether the answer is in fact a multiple of 9.

Suggestions for Teaching the Lesson

Math Facts

DPP Bit E develops the strategy of using doubles to multiply by four. Task F breaks apart numbers for easier multiplication.

Homework and Practice

- After Part 1 of this lesson, **Questions 12–15** on the *Divisibility Rules* Activity Pages may be assigned for homework. Send home students' completed copies of the *100 Chart* for use with these questions. Also assign **Questions 1–2** in the Homework section.

- After Part 2, assign **Questions 3–10** in the Homework section. Send home one or two clean copies of the *100 Chart*.

- DPP Bit C uses skip counting to measure elapsed time. Task D is a game using place value.

Assessment

- Use **Question 6** in the Homework section as an assessment. Ask students to describe how they know a number is divisible by 5 and how they know a number is divisible by 10. Encourage them to use their copies of the *100 Chart,* calculators, and multiplication and division number sentences. Students' emphasis should be on communicating what they know about division by 5 and 10. Review the Student Rubric: *Telling* before assigning **Question 6.** When reviewing students' work, look for the following:

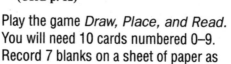

Daily Practice and Problems: Tasks for Lesson 2

D. Task: Play *Draw, Place, and Read*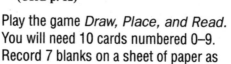
(URG p. 12)

Play the game *Draw, Place, and Read.* You will need 10 cards numbered 0–9. Record 7 blanks on a sheet of paper as shown below.

—, — — —, — — —

1. A caller draws 7 numbers.

2. After each draw, players record the digit drawn in any of the seven places. Once a digit is recorded, it cannot be moved.

3. After all seven draws, the person who makes and reads the highest number earns a point.

F. Task: Break Apart Sevens
(URG p. 13)

One way to solve 8×7 is to break the 7 into $5 + 2$.

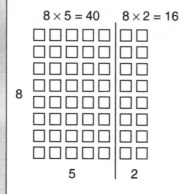

$$8 \times 7 = 40 + 16 = 56$$
$8 \times 5 = 40$ and $8 \times 2 = 16$,
so $8 \times 7 = 40 + 16 = 56$

1. Draw a picture for 8×7 that uses 7 broken into $4 + 3$. Write a number sentence that goes with your picture.

2. Find another way to break up 7. Draw a picture. Write a number sentence for this picture.

3. Write the four number sentences in the fact family for 8×7.

Figure 5: *Multiples of 5 and multiples of 10*

1. Did students mark the multiples of 5 and the multiples of 10 on the *100 Chart?* (See Figure 5.)

2. Did they describe the patterns they saw?

3. Did they compare multiples of 5 and 10? Did they notice that numbers ending in 0 are divisible by 5 *and* 10?

4. Did they include number sentences as examples? (For example, $25 \div 5 = 5$; $5 \times 10 = 50$)

5. Did they mention remainders?

6. Did they use other tools such as a calculator to divide larger numbers by 5 and 10?

7. Did they list keystrokes as a record of how they used the calculator?

• Use Part 3 of the Home Practice as a quiz.

Answers for Part 3 of the Home Practice can be found in the Answer Key at the end of this lesson and at the end of this unit.

Extension

Students may explore divisibility by 4. A number is divisible by 4 if the number formed by the last two digits is divisible by 4. For example, the number formed by the last two digits of 324—24 is divisible by 4.

Name _____ Date _____

Part 3 **Division**
Use the numbers listed below to answer the following questions.

567   85,680   289   27,786   1028   10,782

1. Which numbers are divisible by 2? How did you decide?

2. Which numbers are divisible by 3? How did you decide?

3. Which are divisible by 6? How did you decide?

4. Which are divisible by 5 and 10? How did you decide?

5. Which are divisible by 9? How did you decide?

Part 4 **Addition and Subtraction Practice**
Solve the following problems mentally or using paper and pencil.

A. $210 + 42 =$ _____   B. $360 + 18 =$ _____

C. $350 + 35 =$ _____   D. $480 + 36 =$ _____

E. $180 + 27 =$ _____   F. $270 + 45 =$ _____

G. $330 - 40 =$ _____   H. $280 - 41 =$ _____

I. $445 - 50 =$ _____

86   DAB · Grade 4 · Unit 7   PATTERNS IN MULTIPLICATION

Discovery Assignment Book - Page 86

Homework

You will need a clean copy of the *100 Chart* to complete this homework.

1. Which numbers below are divisible by 2? Tell how you decided.

345   980   1369   1197   3288
9036   2273   1035   8665   2073

2. Which numbers are divisible by 3? Tell how you decided.

3. Which numbers are divisible by 6? Tell how you decided.

4. Which numbers are divisible by 9? Tell how you decided.

5. Are any of the numbers divisible by 2, 3, 6, and 9? Which one(s)?

6. Use a clean copy of a *100 Chart* and a calculator to explore the following.
   A. Skip count by 5s on the *100 Chart*. Mark each multiple of 5. Then, skip count by 10s and mark the multiples of 10.
   B. Describe how you know a number is divisible by 5. In your description, include:
   • Examples of numbers that are divisible by 5.
   • Multiplication sentences and division sentences for those numbers.
   • Descriptions of patterns you see on the *100 Chart*.
   • Any keystrokes you used on the calculator.
   C. Describe how you know a number is divisible by 10. In your description, include:
   • Examples of numbers that are divisible by 10.
   • Multiplication sentences and division sentences for those numbers.
   • Descriptions of patterns you see on the *100 Chart*.
   • Any keystrokes you used on the calculator.

Use the order of operations.

7. $6 \times 7 - 4 \times 8 =$ 8. $1 + 48 \div 8 =$

9. $4 + 7 \times 8 =$ 10. $4 \times 7 - 24 \div 6 =$

Divisibility Rules   SG · Grade 4 · Unit 7 · Lesson 2   189

Student Guide - Page 189

AT A GLANCE

Math Facts and Daily Practice and Problems

DPP item C practices skip counting to measure time. Task D develops number sense. Items E and F develop math facts strategies, using doubles and breaking apart numbers.

Part 1. Divisibility by 2 and 3

1. Read and discuss the introduction on the *Divisibility Rules* Activity Pages in the *Student Guide.*
2. Use *Questions 1–4, 100 Charts,* and calculators to discuss divisibility by 2.
3. Students circle multiples of 2 on *100 Charts* with a blue crayon and explore patterns.
4. Students write multiplication and division number sentences as they explore numbers divisible by 2.
5. Use *Questions 5–10, 100 Charts,* and calculators to discuss divisibility by 3.
6. Students mark multiples of 3 with red Xs and explore patterns.
7. Students write multiplication and division number sentences involving 3.
8. Use *Question 11* to discuss how to tell if a number is divisible by 3.
9. List multiples of three on the board. Emphasize the divisibility rule for 3. List counterexamples as well.
10. Assign *Questions 12–15.*

Part 2. Divisibility by 6 and 9

1. Students refer to the *100 Chart* they completed in Part 1 to explore divisibility by 6.
2. Use *Question 16, 100 Charts,* and calculators to discuss divisibility by 6.
3. List multidigit numbers on the board. Have students identify which are divisible by 6.
4. Use *Question 17* as a discussion question or a journal prompt.
5. Students complete *Questions 18–22.* They explore division by 9.

Homework

1. *Questions 12–15* in the *Student Guide* may be assigned as homework after Part 1.
2. Assign *Questions 1–2* in the Homework section in the *Student Guide* after Part 1.
3. Assign *Questions 3–19* after Part 2. Students need one or two clean copies of the *100 Chart* and a calculator.

Assessment

1. Use *Question 6* in the Homework section as an assessment.
2. Use Part 3 of the Home Practice as a quiz.

Notes:

100 Chart

1	2	3	4	5	6	7	8	9	10
11	12	13	14	15	16	17	18	19	20
21	22	23	24	25	26	27	28	29	30
31	32	33	34	35	36	37	38	39	40
41	42	43	44	45	46	47	48	49	50
51	52	53	54	55	56	57	58	59	60
61	62	63	64	65	66	67	68	69	70
71	72	73	74	75	76	77	78	79	80
81	82	83	84	85	86	87	88	89	90
91	92	93	94	95	96	97	98	99	100

Student Guide

Questions 1–22 (SG pp. 185–188)

1. See Figure 1 in Lesson Guide 2.

2. *In the column with the 8.

3. **A.** 216, 784, 1000, 1358, 2462; These numbers are even. The ones' digit is 0, 2, 4, 6, or 8.

   B. $108 \times 2 = 216$; $216 \div 2 = 108$; $392 \times 2 = 784$; $784 \div 2 = 392$; $500 \times 2 = 1000$; $1000 \div 2 = 500$; $679 \times 2 = 1358$; $1358 \div 2 = 679$; $1231 \times 2 = 2462$; $2462 \div 2 = 1231$

4. A number is divisible by 2 if it is a multiple of 2. Multiples of 2 are even. The ones' digit is 0, 2, 4, 6, or 8.

5. See Figure 2 in Lesson Guide 2.

6. *

7. **A.** Yes; $9 \times 3 = 27$

   B. Yes; $27 \div 3 = 9$

   C. Yes; $17 \times 3 = 51$

   D. Yes; $51 \div 3 = 17$

8. **A.** No; Explanations will vary. 3 and no other whole number will multiply to make 14; 14 is not reached when you skip count by 3s; If you divide 14 by 3, you do not get a whole number answer.

   B. R2; $4 \times 3 + 2 = 14$ or $14 \div 3 = 4$ R2

   C. The calculator does not show a whole number so 14 is not divisible by 3. It shows 4.6666667.

9. 75; $75 \div 3 = 25$

10. **A.** *Predictions will vary. No, 101 does not fall on the diagonals made on the *100 Chart.* On the calculator, $101 \div 3$ does not give a whole number; therefore, 101 is not divisible by 3.

    B. Predictions will vary. Yes, 102 falls on the same diagonal as 84 and 93. On the calculator $102 \div 3 = 34$, a whole number. 102 is divisible by 3.

C. Explanations will vary. If you extend the *100 Chart,* you can see that 117 falls on the diagonal with 90 and 99. On the calculator, $117 \div 3 = 39$, a whole number. 117 is divisible by 3. 116 and 118 are not divisible by 3.

11. *Answers will vary.

12. Answers will vary. A few examples are: 126, 138, 159, 171

13. Answers will vary. A few examples are: 255, 378, 501

14. **A.** 126, 342, 177, 1002, 297, 8775

    B. 126, 342, 1664, 1002, 8770

    C. 126, 342, 1002

15. *Yes; Yes

16. **A.** 126, 342, 1002

    B. *Answers will vary. If the number is divisible by 2 and 3, it is divisible by 6. If the number is even and the sum of its digits is a multiple of 3.

    C. Yes, 12,345,678 is even, and the sum of its digits is a multiple of 3.

17. **A.** *Answers will vary. A few examples are: 174, 186, 204

    B. *Answers will vary. A few examples are: 264, 270, 348

18. 9
    18
    27
    36
    45
    54
    63
    72
    81
    90

19. *

---

*Answers and/or discussion are included in the Lesson Guide.

**Answers for all the Home Practice in the *Discovery Assignment Book* are at the end of the unit.

20. A. 5706

   B. 207

   C. 333

   D. 657

   E. 1287

   F. 3996

   G. 6786

   H. 39,789

21. *

22. A. 144, 747, 2556, 8721, 12,987; The sums of the digits of these numbers are all multiples of 9. Repeatedly adding the digits results in 9.

   B. Using a calculator results in whole numbers for the following: $144 \div 9, 747 \div 9, 2556 \div 9, 8721 \div 9, 12,987 \div 9$.

   C. $144 \div 9 = 16$; $747 \div 9 = 83$; $2556 \div 9 = 284$; $8721 \div 9 = 969$; $12,987 \div 9 = 1443$

Homework (SG p. 189)

Questions 1–10

1. 980; 3288; 9036; They are even numbers. The ones' digit is 0, 2, 4, 6, or 8.

2. 345; 1197; 3288; 9036; 1035; 2073; The sum of the digits in each number is a multiple of 3. Some students might use a calculator. Divide each number by 3 on the calculator. If the answer is a whole number, it is divisible by 3.

3. 3288; 9036; These numbers are divisible by 2 and 3 so they are divisible by 6.

4. 1197; 9036; 1035; The sums of the digits are multiples of 9. If you repeatedly add the digits, you get 9. (For example, $1 + 1 + 9 + 7 = 18$; $1 + 8 = 9$)

5. Yes; 9036

6. A. See Figure 5 in Lesson Guide 2.

   B. *Multiples of 5 end in 0 and 5. The ones' digit is 0 or 5.

   C. *Multiples of 10 end in 0. The ones' digit is 0. If a number is a multiple of 10, it is also a multiple of 5.

7. 10

8. 7

9. 60

10. 24

Discovery Assignment Book

** Home Practice (DAB p. 86)

Part 3. Division

Questions 1–5

1. 85,680; 27,786; 1028; 10,782. Students' explanations will vary. Possible explanations are: all the even numbers are divisible by two or numbers that have a 0, 2, 4, 6, or 8 in the ones' place are divisible by two.

2. 567; 85,680; 27,786; 10,782. Students' explanations will vary. Students might divide each number by 3 and see if there is a remainder or they might add the digits in each number to see if the sum is a multiple of three.

3. 85,680; 27,786; 10,782. Students' explanations will vary. Students should choose all numbers in common between *Questions 1* and *2*. Numbers that are divisible by 2 and 3 are also divisible by 6.

4. 85,680. Students' explanations will vary. Students might say that numbers that have a 0 or a 5 in the ones' place are divisible by 5 and numbers that have a 0 in the ones' place are divisible by 10.

5. 567; 85,680; 10,782. Students' explanations will vary. Students might divide each number by 9 and see if there is a remainder or they might add the digits in each number to see if the sum is a multiple of nine.

*Answers and/or discussion are included in the Lesson Guide.

**Answers for all the Home Practice in the *Discovery Assignment Book* are at the end of the unit.

LESSON GUIDE 3

Oh, No! My Calculator Is Broken

Estimated Class Sessions: 3

Students explore strategies for solving multiplication problems using a calculator. They then complete an open-response problem assessing their problem-solving abilities.

Key Content

- Using efficient strategies for the last six facts.
- Using the calculator efficiently in problem solving.
- Solving open-response problems and communicating solution strategies.

Key Vocabulary

product

Curriculum Sequence

Before This Unit

Student Rubrics. The Student Rubric: *Solving* was used to assess student problem solving in Unit 5. Students used the Student Rubric: *Knowing* to guide their problem-solving strategies in Unit 6 Lesson 6.

After This Unit

Student Rubrics. All of the Student Rubrics (*Solving, Knowing,* and *Telling*) will be used to guide students as they solve open-response problems in Units 8 and 16. The rubrics will be used in other activities and assessment lessons to guide students as they solve problems.

Daily Practice and Problems: Bits for Lesson 3

G. Order of Operations (URG p. 14)

Remember the order of operations as you do the following problems. Do these problems mentally or with pencil and paper, not calculators.

A. $3 \times 5 + 5 =$ 　　 B. $6 + 20 \div 4 =$

C. $9 + 8 \times 6 =$ 　　 D. $6 \div 2 + 7 \times 6 =$

E. $4 \times 8 + 1 \times 2 =$

F. $10 - 3 \times 3 =$

I. Divisible by 2, 3, or 6? (URG p. 15)

1. Which of the following numbers are divisible by 2?

   762　　1025　　8031　　4296　　1111

2. Which are multiples of 3?

3. Which numbers have 6 as a factor?

K. Finding Medians (URG p. 15)

Here is Jackie's data for a paper towel experiment. She dropped water on one sheet of three different brands of paper towels (Ecotowel, Cheap-O, and Handy). She dropped three drops of water on each towel. The water spread out and made a spot. Jackie then measured the area of each spot of water in square centimeters.

T Type of Towel	*A* Area (in sq cm)			
	Trial 1	Trial 2	Trial 3	Median
Ecotowel	23 sq cm	20 sq cm	21 sq cm	
Cheap-O	37 sq cm	36 sq cm	41 sq cm	
Handy	11 sq cm	10 sq cm	12 sq cm	

Find the median area for each type of towel.

DPP Tasks and Challenge are on page 58.
Suggestions for using the DPPs are on page 58.

Materials List

Print Materials for Students

	Math Facts and Daily Practice and Problems	Assessment Activity	Homework	Written Assessment
Student Books — Student Guide		Student Rubrics: *Knowing* Appendix A, *Solving* Appendix B and Inside Back Cover, ⊙ and *Oh, No! My Calculator Is Broken* Pages 190–192		
Discovery Assignment Book			Home Practice Part 4 Page 86	
Teacher Resources — Facts Resource Guide	DPP Items 7G, 7H & 7J			
Unit Resource Guide ⊙	DPP Items G–L Pages 14–16 ⊙			*The Broken Calculator* Page 60, 1 per student

⊙ *available on Teacher Resource CD*

All Transparency Masters, Blackline Masters, and Assessment Blackline Masters in the Unit Resource Guide are on the Teacher Resource CD.

Supplies for Each Student

calculator

Materials for the Teacher

Poster or transparency of the Student Rubric: *Knowing* (Teacher Implementation Guide, Assessment section)
Poster or transparency of the Student Rubric: *Solving* (Teacher Implementation Guide, Assessment section)
TIMS Multidimensional Rubric (Teacher Implementation Guide, Assessment section)

Developing the Activity

Part 1. Oh, No! My Calculator Is Broken

Ask students to imagine that some of the keys on their calculators do not work. Read the vignette on the *Oh, No! My Calculator Is Broken* Activity Pages in the *Student Guide*. Discuss the strategies that John, Keenya, and Grace use to solve the problem 6 × 8 using their broken calculators.

John's strategy is to use break-apart facts. Students may remember doing break-apart facts using rectangles in third grade and the Daily Practice and Problems. Illustrate John's strategy using break-apart rectangles, as shown in Figure 6.

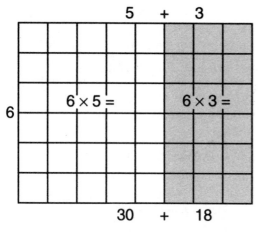

Figure 6: *Break-apart rectangles for 6 × 8 = 48*

Students are asked to use their calculators to carry out each of the suggested strategies in the *Student Guide*. They should all result in the same answer, 48. This validates the many strategies that students can use to find a solution to a multiplication problem. Encourage students to record their keystrokes as shown on the activity pages.

For *Questions 1–5,* students imagine that different keys on their calculators do not work. They find a strategy, using their calculators, to answer various multiplication problems. Students may use strategies suggested in the vignette or they may develop different strategies. Students can work on these problems independently or with a partner; however, it is important to provide time for the class to discuss their various strategies. This discussion time provides an opportunity for students to hear about and experiment with strategies that may be more efficient than their own. For example, to find 6 × 7 in two ways without the ⑥ key (*Question 2A*), students can record these two sets of keystrokes:

③ × ⑦ + ③ × ⑦ and
⑦ + ⑦ + ⑦ + ⑦ + ⑦
+ ⑦ .

Oh, No! My Calculator Is Broken

Multiplication

Discuss

Mrs. Dewey passed out calculators to her class. She asked the class to use the calculators to do 6 × 8. John pressed: ⑥ × ⑧ = .

He soon realized the ⑧ key on his calculator was broken. Both Keenya and Grace tried their calculators. They each found that the × keys on their calculators were broken. In fact, all of the calculators in the class had keys that didn't work. Mrs. Dewey said, "Some of the keys on these calculators have been disconnected. Think about how you can use your calculator to multiply 6 × 8."

John knew that he could break apart 8 into 5 + 3. He could then multiply 6 × 5 and 6 × 3 and add the two products together to get 6 × 8. To show his solution, John recorded the following keystrokes:

⑥ × ⑤ + ⑥ × ③ =

Student Guide - Page 190

Since the × key was broken on Keenya's calculator, she decided to turn 6 × 8 into an addition problem. Keenya recorded the following keystrokes:

⑧ + ⑧ + ⑧ + ⑧ + ⑧ + ⑧ =

Grace knew that 6 × 8 would be twice the answer to 3 × 8. "Since 3 × 8 = 24, I can use my calculator to add 24 + 24 to find the answer for 6 × 8." She recorded these keystrokes:

㉔ + ㉔ =

With your calculator try each of the strategies suggested by Grace, John, and Keenya. Do you get the same answer with each strategy?

Explore

1. A. Pretend you are using Keenya's calculator and the × key is broken. Give a different list of keystrokes to find 6 × 8. Record your keystrokes on your own paper.
    B. Pretend you are using John's calculator and the ⑧ key is broken. Give a different list of keystrokes to find 6 × 8. Record your keystrokes on your own paper.

Use a calculator to do the problems below two different ways. For each problem, record the keystrokes you pressed.

2. Imagine that the ⑥ key on your calculator is broken.
    A. 6 × 7 =   B. 6 × 4 =
3. Imagine that the ⑦ key on your calculator is broken.
    A. 7 × 8 =   B. 6 × 7 =
4. Imagine that the ② key on your calculator is broken. Use your calculator to find the answer to this problem in two ways: 4 × 2 × 7 =. Record your keystrokes.
5. Imagine that the × key on your calculator is broken. Use your calculator to find the answer to each problem in two ways. Record your keystrokes.
    A. 9 × 6 =   B. 9 × 7 =

Student Guide - Page 191

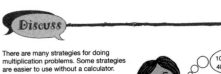

Discuss

There are many strategies for doing multiplication problems. Some strategies are easier to use without a calculator.

Maya found a strategy for multiplying 9 × 4. She said, "First I will multiply 10 × 4, then if I subtract 4 from 40, I will get 9 × 4."

10 × 4 = 40
40 − 4 = ?

6. **A.** Why is Maya multiplying 10 × 4?
   B. Why is she subtracting 4?

7. How would you explain Maya's strategy to a friend?

8. Use Maya's strategy to solve 9 × 7. Explain your thinking.

9. What are some strategies you could use to solve 12 × 8?

Addition and Subtraction

Shannon found an old calculator. When she tried the calculator, she found that only the clear key and these keys worked:

[8] [3] [−] [+] [=]

She found that she could get the number 2 on her display by pressing:
[8][−][3][−][3][=], but she wondered if she could figure out a way to get the number 1 on her display.

10. Help Shannon think of a strategy she could use to get a 1 on her calculator display.

11. What keystrokes can Shannon use to get the number 55 on her calculator display? Remember, you can only use the 6 keys that work.

Student Guide - Page 192

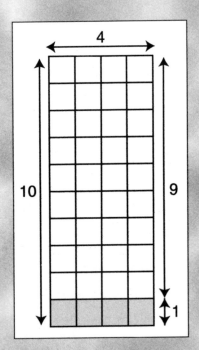

Figure 7: *Since 10 × 4 = 40 and 1 × 4 = 4,*
9 × 4 = 40 − 4 = 36

For *Questions 6–9,* students consider other strategies. In a short vignette introducing these questions, Maya says that she can solve 9 × 4 by first multiplying 10 × 4 and then subtracting 4 from the product. Students are asked to explain this strategy in *Question 7.* Help students see that 9 groups of 4 is 4 less than 10 groups of 4 using multiplication rectangles, as shown in Figure 7. Since 10 × 4 may be an easier fact to recall, students can find this product and then take 4 away to find 9 × 4.

Students will use their "broken" calculators to find different numbers using addition and subtraction in *Questions 10–11.* This short activity is a lead-in to Part 2 of this lesson, the assessment problem *The Broken Calculator.* To solve *Question 11,* students must get the number 55 on their calculators using only the clear key and these five keys: [8] [3] [+] [−] [=]. One possible solution is 88 − 33 =. Be sure students understand that they can use any of these keys as many times as they like and that multidigit numbers such as 83 and 88 are allowed.

Part 2. The Broken Calculator

In this open-response assessment problem, students generate all of the numbers 1 through 50 on their calculator display using only the clear key and the following five keys: [2] [5] [+] [−] [=].

Begin by reading the vignette on *The Broken Calculator* Assessment Blackline Master together. Review the Student Rubrics: *Knowing* and *Solving* using transparencies or posters. Explain that student work will be scored using these two rubrics.

As you observe students working, you may need to help students get started or clarify students' understanding of the problem. Keep a record of the type of help you give to individual students so you can use the information as you score their work. For example, if a student needs help organizing the number sentences, you may reduce his or her score on the Solving dimension. It is also appropriate to make comments on students' written work and then give them an opportunity to revise their work based on your comments.

Once students have completed this task, assess their work using the Solving and Knowing dimensions of the *TIMS Multidimensional Rubric.* To help you use the rubric to score your students' work, the following questions have been developed.

These questions are based on the Solving and Knowing dimensions, but are specific to this assessment task.

Solving:

Do students identify the elements of the problem?
>Do they only use the keys given in the problem?
>Do they form numbers with multiple digits such as 22, 25, 52, and 55?
>Do students look for all 50 numbers?

Do students use problem-solving strategies that are systematic, complete, and efficient? For example, do they make use of "chaining" strategies? A chaining strategy makes use of one solution to find solutions for other numbers (such as $5 + 5 + 2 = 12$, so $5 + 5 + 2 + 2 = 14$ or $55 - 5 = 50$, so $55 - 5 - 5 = 45$ and $55 - 5 - 2 = 48$).

Do students organize relevant information? Do they list the number sentences in order from 1 to 50?

Do students persist in the problem-solving process?
>Do students complete the task?
>Do students find more than one solution for any of the numbers?

Do students look back at their solutions to see if their solutions were correct?

Knowing:

Do students understand the task's mathematical concepts and applications?
>Do students use repeated addition and subtraction to form numbers?
>Do students use place value concepts to form numbers such as 55 and 52?

Do students translate between words and symbols readily and without errors? Do they write correct number sentences? For example, $5 + 5 + 2 = 12$ is a true statement, while $5 + 5 = 10 + 2 = 12$ is not.

Do students use tools such as calculators and procedures correctly?
>Do students use calculators correctly and appropriately?
>Do students add and subtract correctly?

Do students use the knowledge of the math facts correctly?

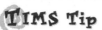

TIMS Tip

This assessment problem is intended for students working independently. However, you may want to provide a short amount of time before students begin working on their own to discuss the task with a partner. When students are ready to begin, remind them that they will need to keep track of the numbers between 1 and 50 that they find, but do not give any suggestions as to how they should do this. After about 15–20 minutes of independent work, you may want to give students 5–7 minutes to discuss their work with their partner. This will provide an opportunity for students to make revisions or to rethink their strategies before they continue. After this short discussion, students should return to their independent work.

The following samples of student work for *Question 1* have been scored using these two dimensions. The cells in the Solving dimension corresponding to the statement "Relates the problem solution to previously encountered mathematics and makes connections that are . . ." are not used to score students' work. Evidence that students related this problem to other mathematics is not easily obtained for this task.

Written work from Student A:

$$5+5 = \boxed{10} - 2 - 2 - 2 \boxed{4}$$
$$5 - 2 = \boxed{3}$$
$$5 + 2 = \boxed{7}$$
$$5 + 5 + 2 = \boxed{12}$$

$$5 - 2 - 2 = \boxed{1}$$
$$2 + 2 + 2 = \boxed{6} \boxed{5} \boxed{1}$$
$$5 - 5 = 0 \angle 2 \angle 5$$
$$5 + 5 = \boxed{10} - 2 = \boxed{8}$$
$$5 - 2 + 5 = \boxed{8}$$

$$5 + 5 + 5 + 5 + 5 = \boxed{25} - 5 - 2 = \boxed{18}$$

$$25 + 2 = \boxed{27}$$
$$25 - 5 = \boxed{20}$$

$$25 + 25 = \boxed{50} - 5 = \boxed{45}$$
$$25 - 2 = \boxed{5}$$
$$52 - 2 = \boxed{50}$$
$$52 - 11 = \boxed{51}$$
$$55 - 5 = \boxed{50}$$
$$25 + 5 = \boxed{30}$$
$$52 - 5 = \boxed{47}$$
$$2 + 2 + 2 + 2 + 2 = \boxed{10}$$

On this task, Student A is at level 2 on the Solving dimension. In his written paragraph (not shown here), this student identified some of the elements of this problem; however, he did not understand the relationships among these elements. For example, this student used $5 + 2 = 7$, but did not build upon this to show that $5 + 2 + 2 = 9$. He was also able to find that $25 + 25 - 5 = 50 - 5 = 45$, but did not continue this pattern by continuing to subtract 5 in order to get 40, 35, and 30. The strategies that this student chose were incomplete. He did not organize his work and, as a result, found more than one solution for some numbers and no solutions for others. This student did not continue to work until he had found a solution for each number.

Solving	Level 4	Level 3	Level 2	Level 1
Identifies these elements of the problem and their relationships to one another	All major elements identified	Most elements identified ✗	Some, but shows little understanding of relationships	Few or none
Uses problem-solving strategies which are . . .	Systematic, complete, efficient, and possibly elegant	Systematic and nearly complete, but not efficient	Incomplete or unsystematic ✗	Not evident or inappropriate
Organizes relevant information . . .	Systematically and efficiently	Systematically, with minor errors	Unsystematically	Not at all ✗
Relates the problem and solution to previously encountered mathematics and makes connections that are . . . (NA)	At length, elegant, and meaningful	Evident	Brief or logically unsound	Not evident
Persists in the problem-solving process . . .	At length	Until a solution is reached	Briefly ✗	Not at all
Looks back to examine the reasonableness of the solution and draws conclusions that are . . .	Insightful and comprehensive	Correct ✗	Incorrect or logically unsound	Not present

Knowing	Level 4	Level 3	Level 2	Level 1
Understands the task's mathematical concepts, their properties and applications . . .	Completely	Nearly completely ✗	Partially	Not at all
Translates between words, pictures, symbols, tables, graphs, and real situations . . .	Readily and without errors	With minor errors ✗	With major errors	Not at all
Uses tools (measuring devices, graphs, tables, calculators, etc.) and procedures . . .	Correctly and efficiently	Correctly or with minor errors ✗	Incorrectly	Not at all
Uses knowledge of the facts of mathematics (geometry definitions, math facts, etc.) . . .	Correctly	With minor errors ✗	With major errors	Not at all

Figure 8: *Student A's work scored using two dimensions of the* TIMS Multidimensional Rubric

On the Knowing dimension of the rubric, Student A is at a level 3. While this student appears to understand only partially the mathematical applications in this problem since he did not look for solutions in any apparent order, he did use the math facts correctly. This student also showed evidence of *chaining* in his solutions. For example, he found a solution for both 10 and 4 using $5 + 5 = 10$ ($5 + 5 = 10 - 2 - 2 - 2 = 4$), and for both 50 and 45 using $25 + 25 = 50$ ($25 + 25 = 50 - 5 = 45$). However, note that his number sentences are not true statements. Correct number sentences would read $5 + 5 - 2 - 2 - 2 = 10 - 2 - 2 - 2 = 4$ and $25 + 25 - 5 = 50 - 5 = 45$. He used the calculator correctly to check his work, but was not always able to translate accurately between the work done on the calculator and the work done using paper and pencil. However, he did show some understanding of place value by using numbers such as 25, 52, and 55 to help find solutions to some of the larger numbers.

Student B:

5, 10, 8, 13, 18, 23, 28,
33, 38, 43, 48, 53

		15 $5+5+5=$	30	15 $5+5+5+4$ $5+5+5$
			31	$9+5+5=$ 4 $+5+5+5$
1. $5-2-2=$		16 $5+5+2+7+2-$		46 $+5=$
2. $5+2-5=2-2=$		17 $5+5+5+2=$	32	47
3. $5-2=$		18 $5+5+2+2+2+2$	33	48
4. $2+2=$		19 $5+5+2+2+5=$	34	49
5. $5+5-5=$		20 $5+5+5+5=$	35 $5+5+5+5+$ $5+5=$	50 $5+5+5+$ $5+5+5+5$
6. $2+2+2=$		21 $5+5+5+2+2=$ 36		
7. $5+2=$		22 $5+5+5$	37	
8. $5+5-2=$		23	38	
9. $5+5+5-2-2-2=24$			39	
10 $5+5=$		25 $5+5+5+5+5$	40 $5+5+5$ $+5+5+5$ $5+5+5+$
11 $5+5+5-2-2=$ 26			41	$5=$
12 $5+5+2=$		27	42	
13 $5+5+5-2=$ 28			43	
14 $5+5+2+2=$		29	44	

On the Solving dimension, Student B is at level 2. Initially, this student just began pushing random numbers into the calculator and then began to list these numbers. This student clearly did not understand what the problem was asking for and needed support from the teacher to begin a systematic approach to finding solutions. The student also had to be given a table to organize her solutions. She was unable to find a solution for each number and quickly gave up once she found some of the more obvious numbers (the multiples of 5).

Solving	Level 4	Level 3	Level 2	Level 1
Identifies these elements of the problem and their relationships to one another	All major elements identified	Most elements identified	Some, but shows little understanding of relationships	Few or none
Uses problem-solving strategies which are . . .	Systematic, complete, efficient, and possibly elegant	Systematic and nearly complete, but not efficient	Incomplete or unsystematic *– only after help & organizational support*	~~Not evident or inappropriate~~
Organizes relevant information . . .	Systematically and efficiently	Systematically, with minor errors	~~Unsystematically~~ *structure given*	Not at all
Relates the problem and solution to previously encountered mathematics and makes connections that are . . . *NA*	At length, elegant, and meaningful	Evident	Brief or logically unsound	Not evident
Persists in the problem-solving process . . .	At length	Until a solution is reached	~~Briefly~~	Not at all
Looks back to examine the reasonableness of the solution and draws conclusions that are . . .	Insightful and comprehensive	~~Correct~~	Incorrect or logically unsound	Not present

(Level 2 circled in Solving table)

Knowing	Level 4	Level 3	Level 2	Level 1
Understands the task's mathematical concepts, their properties and applications . . .	Completely	Nearly completely ~~Partially~~		Not at all
Translates between words, pictures, symbols, tables, graphs, and real situations . . .	Readily and without errors	~~With minor errors~~	With major errors	Not at all
Uses tools (measuring devices, graphs, tables, calculators, etc.) and procedures . . .	Correctly and efficiently	~~Correctly or with minor errors~~	Incorrectly	Not at all
Uses knowledge of the facts of mathematics (geometry definitions, math facts, etc.) . . .	Correctly	~~With minor errors~~	With major errors	Not at all

(Level 3 circled in Knowing table)

Figure 9: *Student B's work scored using two dimensions of the* TIMS Multidimensional Rubric

On the Knowing dimension of the rubric, Student B is at level 3. She demonstrated a partial understanding of the mathematical applications. This student showed little evidence of chaining in order to find solutions, although she did use repeated addition to find all of the multiples of 5 from 10 to 50. All the numbers are not correct. This student used the calculator correctly; however, she was not efficient in its use. This was evident in observing the student as she found the multiples of 5. Rather than finding 10 and then continuing to add 5 to find the other multiples, this student did each problem separately and out of order. This student did not use knowledge of place value to find the solutions for the larger numbers efficiently. For example, she did not use numbers like 22, 25, 52, and 55 to help find solutions.

Student C:

1. $5-2-2=1$	12. $5+5+2=12$	23. $5+5+5+5+5-2=23$	34. $25+5+2+2=34$	45 $55-5-5=45$
2. $5+2-5=2$	13. $5+5+5-2=13$	24. $5+5+5+5+2+2=24$	35. $25+5+5=35$	46. $55-2-5-2=46$
3. $5-2=3$	14. $5+5+2+2=14$	25. $5+5+5+5+5=25$	36. $25+5+2+2+2=36$	47. $52-5=47$
4. $5+2-5+2=4$	15. $5+5+5=15$	26. $5+5+5+5+2+2+2=26$	37. $5+5+5+5+5+5+5-2=37$	48 $55-5-2=48$
5. $5+2-2=5$	16. $5+5+5+5-2-2=16$	27. $5+5+5+5+5+2=27$	38. $5+5+5+5+5+5+5+2+2+2+2=$	49 $55-2-2-2=49$
6. $5+5-2-2=6$	17. $5+5+5+2=17$	28. $5+5+5+5+2+2+2+2=28$	39. $5+5+5+5+5+5+5+2+2=39$	50 $55-5=50$
7. $5+2=7$	18. $5+5+5+5-2=18$	29. $5+5+5+5+5+2+2=29$	40. $55-5-5-5=40$	
8 $5+5-2=8$	19. $5+5+5+5+5-2-2-2=19$	30. $52-22=30$	41. $55-5-5-2-2=41$	
9 $5+5+5-2-2-2=9$	20. $5+5+5+5=20$	31. $25+2+2+2=31$	42. $55-5-5-5+2=42$	
10. $5+5=10$	21. $5+5+5+5+5-2-2=21$	32. $25+5+2=32$	43. $55+2-5-5=43$	
11. $5+2+2+2=11$	22. $5+5+5+5+2=22$	33. $55-22=33$	44. $52-2-2-2-2=44$	

Solving	Level 4	Level 3	Level 2	Level 1
Identifies these elements of the problem and their relationships to one another	All major elements identified	Most elements identified	Some, but shows little understanding of relationships	Few or none
Uses problem-solving strategies which are . . .	Systematic, complete, efficient, and possibly elegant	Systematic and nearly complete, but not efficient	Incomplete or unsystematic	Not evident or inappropriate
Organizes relevant information . . .	Systematically and efficiently	Systematically, with minor errors	Unsystematically	Not at all
Relates the problem and solution to previously encountered mathematics and makes connections that are . . .	At length, elegant, and meaningful	Evident	Brief or logically unsound	Not evident
Persists in the problem-solving process . . .	At length	Until a solution is reached	Briefly	Not at all
Looks back to examine the reasonableness of the solution and draws conclusions that are . . .	Insightful and comprehensive	Correct	Incorrect or logically unsound	Not present

Knowing	Level 4	Level 3	Level 2	Level 1
Understands the task's mathematical concepts, their properties and applications . . .	Completely	Nearly completely	Partially	Not at all
Translates between words, pictures, symbols, tables, graphs, and real situations . . .	Readily and without errors	With minor errors	With major errors	Not at all
Uses tools (measuring devices, graphs, tables, calculators, etc.) and procedures . . .	Correctly and efficiently	Correctly or with minor errors	Incorrectly	Not at all
Uses knowledge of the facts of mathematics (geometry definitions, math facts, etc.) . . .	Correctly	With minor errors	With major errors	Not at all

Figure 10: *Student C's work scored using two dimensions of the* TIMS Multidimensional Rubric

Student C is at level 4 on both the Solving dimension of the rubric and the Knowing dimension. This student understood the many relationships between the numbers and operations he was allowed to use to find solutions. The strategies he used included place value applications ($55 - 22 = 33$ and $25 + 5 + 5 = 35$). He organized his work systematically and efficiently and continued to work on the problem until a solution was reached for each number, although he did not find more than one solution for any number. He used the calculator correctly and showed evidence of chaining strategies as seen in his solution for numbers 40 through 43. He clearly understands the math facts and used patterns in the facts to find many of the solutions.

Journal Prompt

How is knowing more than one strategy for finding a solution to a problem helpful? Give examples of times you have solved a problem in more than one way.

Daily Practice and Problems:
Tasks and Challenge for Lesson 3

H. Challenge: *Operation Target:*
1, 3, 6, 9 (URG p. 14)

Play *Operation Target*.

* Use the four digits 1, 3, 6, 9, and the four operations $(+, -, \times, \div)$ to make as many numbers as you can.

* In each number sentence, you must use each of the four digits exactly once.

* Use any operation more than once or not at all.

* You can make 2-digit numbers by putting two digits together.

* No fractions or decimals are allowed.

For example: $1 + 63 \div 9 = 8$

1. What is the largest number you can make?

2. What is the smallest number you can make?

3. Make the numbers 1 to 10.

J. Task: **Story Solving** (URG p. 15)

Write a story for 6×8. Draw a picture for your story and label it with a number sentence.

L. Task: **Estimating Length**
(URG p. 16)

1. Estimate the length and width of your classroom in centimeters. Write down your estimates and be ready to share your estimation strategy with the class.

2. After everyone has made his or her estimate, the class will measure the length and width of the room.

3. Find 10% of the actual length. Is your estimate within 10% of the length? Show how you know.

Suggestions for Teaching the Lesson

Math Facts

DPP items G and H review the order of operations. Task J practices math facts strategies as students write a story.

Homework and Practice

* DPP Bit I practices divisibility rules, Bit K reviews finding medians, and Task L provides practice in estimation.

* Assign Home Practice Part 4 for practice with addition and subtraction.

Answers for Part 4 of the Home Practice can be found in the Answer Key at the end of this lesson and at the end of this unit.

Assessment

Part 2 *The Broken Calculator* is an assessment activity. Each student's work can be put into the student's portfolio folder so it can be used to show growth over time. This work can be compared to student work on *A Letter to Myrna* in Unit 2 and *Professor Peabody Invents a Ball* in Unit 5.

Name _____ Date _____

Part 3 Division
Use the numbers listed below to answer the following questions.

567   85,680   289   27,786   1028   10,782

1. Which numbers are divisible by 2? How did you decide?

2. Which numbers are divisible by 3? How did you decide?

3. Which are divisible by 6? How did you decide?

4. Which are divisible by 5 and 10? How did you decide?

5. Which are divisible by 9? How did you decide?

Part 4 Addition and Subtraction Practice
Solve the following problems mentally or using paper and pencil.

A. $210 + 42 =$ _____   B. $360 + 18 =$ _____

C. $350 + 35 =$ _____   D. $480 + 36 =$ _____

E. $180 + 27 =$ _____   F. $270 + 45 =$ _____

G. $330 - 40 =$ _____   H. $280 - 41 =$ _____

I. $445 - 50 =$ _____

86   DAB · Grade 4 · Unit 7   PATTERNS IN MULTIPLICATION

Discovery Assignment Book - Page 86

Challenge students to find the numbers 86, 144, and 999 using just the clear key and the following keys on their calculators: | 2 | | 5 | | + | | − | | = |

AT A GLANCE

Math Facts and Daily Practice and Problems

DPP Bit G reviews order of operations and Challenge H uses a game to develop number sense using order of operations. Bit I reviews divisibility rules and Task J asks for a math story. Bit K reviews finding medians and Task L practices estimation.

Part 1. Oh, No! My Calculator Is Broken

1. Read the vignette on the first *Oh, No! My Calculator Is Broken* Activity Page in the *Student Guide.* Discuss the strategies used by each child to find a solution to 6 × 8 using a broken calculator.
2. Students complete *Questions 1–5* either independently or with a partner. Provide time to discuss strategies used to find solutions.
3. Discuss Maya's strategy for multiplying 9 × 4 by working on *Questions 6–8.*
4. Students complete *Question 9* independently.
5. Discuss how to find numbers on the calculator using addition and subtraction *(Questions 10–11).*

Part 2. The Broken Calculator

1. Read the vignette on *The Broken Calculator* Assessment Blackline Master, which introduces this assessment activity.
2. Review the Student Rubrics: *Knowing* and *Solving* with your class.
3. Students work on the problem until they have completed their solutions.

Homework

Assign Home Practice Part 4.

Assessment

1. Score student work using the Solving and Knowing dimensions of the *TIMS Multidimensional Rubric.*
2. Students place scored work in their portfolios.

Notes:

The Broken Calculator

Brandon and John found an old calculator. John tried the calculator and found that only the clear key and five other keys worked:

"I have an idea," said John. "Let's see if we can use the keys that we have to make all of the numbers from 1 to 50."

1. Help John and Brandon. See if you can make all of the numbers from 1 to 50 on the calculator display using just these six keys. You may use each key more than once, or not at all. Make a list and explain what keystrokes you need to produce each number. Remember, you may only use the keys listed above—the others are broken.
2. When you have finished making your list, write a paragraph explaining all of the strategies that you used to find your solutions.
3. Make 83 using these keys. Show your keystrokes. Explain your strategy.

Use the Student Rubrics: *Knowing* and *Solving* to help you as you work these problems.

Student Guide

Questions 1–11 (SG pp. 191–192)

Answers will vary for *Questions 1–5.* One or two possible solutions are provided for each.

1. **A.** $16 + 16 + 16 =$

    B. $6 \times 6 + 6 \times 2 =$

2. **A.** $3 \times 7 + 3 \times 7 =$ or $7 + 7 + 7 + 7 + 7 + 7 =$

    B. $3 \times 4 + 3 \times 4 =$ or $4 + 4 + 4 + 4 + 4 + 4 =$

3. **A.** $5 \times 8 + 2 \times 8 =$ or $8 + 8 + 8 + 8 + 8 + 8 + 8 =$

    B. $5 \times 6 + 2 \times 6 =$ or $6 + 6 + 6 + 6 + 6 + 6 + 6 =$

4. $4 \times 7 + 4 \times 7 =$ or $14 \times 4 =$

5. **A.** $9 + 9 + 9 + 9 + 9 + 9 =$ or $27 + 27 =$ or $60 - 6 =$

    B. $7 + 7 + 7 + 7 + 7 + 7 + 7 + 7 + 7 + 7 =$ or $70 - 7 =$

6. **A.** 10×4 is easier than 9×4

    B. *She had one too many fours. See Figure 7 in Lesson Guide 3.

7. *

8. $10 \times 7 = 70; 70 - 7 = 63$

9. Answers will vary. $10 \times 8 + 2 \times 8 = 80 + 16 = 96$

10. $3 + 3 + 3 - 8 = 1$

11. $88 - 33 = 55$

Discovery Assignment Book

**Home Practice (DAB p. 86)

Part 4. Addition and Subtraction Practice

Questions A–I

  A. 252

  B. 378

  C. 385

  D. 516

  E. 207

  F. 315

  G. 290

  H. 239

  I. 395

Unit Resource Guide

The Broken Calculator (URG p. 60)

Questions 1–3

1. See Lesson Guide 3 for sample student work.

2. Students' solution strategies will vary.

3. Students' keystrokes and strategies will vary. A possible set of keystrokes for 83 is shown: $55 + 22 + 2 + 2 + 2 = 83$.

---

*Answers and/or discussion are included in the Lesson Guide.
**Answers for all the Home Practice in the *Discovery Assignment Book* are at the end of the unit.

M. More Doubles (URG p. 16)

1. A. $3 \times 7 =$

   B. $21 + 21 =$

   C. $6 \times 7 =$

2. A. $3 \times 8 =$

   B. $24 + 24 =$

   C. $6 \times 8 =$

3. A. $3 \times 4 =$

   B. $12 + 12 =$

   C. $6 \times 4 =$

What patterns do you see? Describe a strategy for multiplying a number by 6.

O. Multiplying by 10 (URG p. 17)

Do these problems in your head.

A. $7 \times 80 =$	B. $6 \times 400 =$
C. $8000 \times 6 =$	D. $700 \times 4 =$
E. $n \times 60 = 420$	F. $800 \times n = 3200$
G. $10 \times 700 =$	H. $0 \times 600 =$

DPP Task and Challenge are on page 67.
Suggestions for using the DPPs are on page 67.

LESSON GUIDE

Multiplying by 10s

Estimated Class Sessions:
2

Students use base-ten pieces to develop an understanding of multiplication as repeated addition. They look for patterns when multiplying a one-digit number by multiples of tens, hundreds, thousands, and ten thousands. They use unknowns in number sentences. In Lesson 7 students will multiply two multidigit numbers that end in zero. You may wish to combine this lesson with Lesson 7.

Key Content

- Understanding multiplication as repeated addition.
- Using patterns to multiply numbers with ending zeros.
- Using unknowns in number sentences.

Key Vocabulary

multiple
products

Curriculum Sequence

After This Unit

Students will further explore multiplying by multiples of 10 in Unit 11.

Materials List

Print Materials for Students

	Math Facts and Daily Practice and Problems	Activity	Homework	Written Assessment
Student Books				
Student Guide		*Multiplying by 10s* Pages 193–195	*Multiplying by 10s* Homework Section Pages 195–196	
Discovery Assignment Book				Home Practice Part 5 Page 87
Teacher Resources				
Facts Resource Guide ⊙	DPP Items 7M, 7N & 7O			
Unit Resource Guide ⊙	DPP Items M–P Pages 16–18			
Generic Section ⊙		*Base-Ten Board Parts 1 and 2,* 1 per student pair and *Small Multiplication Tables,* or completed *Multiplication Facts I Know* charts, 1 per student		

⊙ *available on Teacher Resource CD*

All Transparency Masters, Blackline Masters, and Assessment Blackline Masters in the Unit Resource Guide are on the Teacher Resource CD.

Supplies for Each Student Pair

set of base-ten pieces
calculators

Materials for the Teacher

Transparency of *Base-Ten Board Part 1* Blackline Master (Unit Resource Guide, Generic Section)
Transparency of *Recording Sheet* Blackline Master (Unit Resource Guide, Generic Section)
overhead base-ten pieces, optional

Content Note

Instead of calling *n* an unknown, we could also refer to it as a variable. In number sentences, a variable is a symbol that stands for some unknown value (values).

Developing the Activity

Explore multiplication by ten using base-ten pieces. Display base-ten pieces on a transparency of the *Base-Ten Board Part 1* Blackline Master, a magnetic board, or on a table. Pose the following problem:

- *If we have 10 groups of 3 chocos, how many chocos do we have?*

Students may offer more than one way to solve this problem. Students may suggest using 10 groups of 3 bits. Place 10 groups of 3 bits on the overhead *Base-Ten Board.* Ask:

- *How can we use the Fewest Pieces Rule to represent this amount?*

Children should find that 10 groups of 3 bits equals 3 skinnies. Remind students to exchange 10 bits for a skinny. The 3 skinnies should be placed in the skinnies column. On the board, write $10 \times 3 = 30$. Make sure students realize that when we write 30 we mean either 3 skinnies and 0 bits or 30 bits.

Students may suggest another solution strategy. Since a skinny is 10 times larger than 1 bit, when we multiply 3 bits by 10, we get 3 skinnies. One bit multiplied by 10 gives 1 skinny, the second bit multiplied by 10 gives 1 skinny, and the third bit multiplied by ten gives us 1 skinny—10×3 bits = 3 skinnies or 30. When we multiply by ten, everything moves over a column to the left. This idea will be further developed in Unit 11.

Discuss the use of an unknown in a number sentence. For example, instead of asking, "*How much is 10 groups of 3 chocos?*" we could write a number sentence that asks this question. For this problem, we can write $10 \times 3 = n$, and then ask, "*What is the value of* n*?*"

Point out that *n* stands for some number. We could use any other letter if we wished, but we use *n* here because it reminds us that it is some number. What number should *n* be so that the sentence above is true? Since $10 \times 3 = 30$, *n* is 30.

Remind students of the commutative property of multiplication or *turn-around facts.* For example, what if we took 3 groups of 10 instead of 10 groups of 3? 3 groups of 10 bits can be put on the overhead in a three-by-ten array:

```
 .  .  .  .  .  .  .  .  .  .
 .  .  .  .  .  .  .  .  .  .
 .  .  .  .  .  .  .  .  .  .
```

In Unit 4, students learned that an array with 3 rows of 10 dots can be rotated to yield 10 rows of 3 dots. That is, $3 \times 10 = 10 \times 3$. Children know these as turn-around facts. Discuss with them what is easier for them, to think of 3 groups of 10 or 10 groups of 3. Since counting by 10s is easy, they might want to think about turn-around facts in doing these problems. Ask:

- *What if we had 20 groups of 3 bits? A number sentence that describes this question is $20 \times 3 = $ n. What value of* n *makes the sentence true?*

Students should find this is 60 bits or 6 skinnies and 0 bits. Again we can also say 3 groups of 20 bits (3×20 bits $= 60$ bits or 6 skinnies). Record $20 \times 3 = 60$.

Repeat the activity with some more multiplication problems. For example, say:

- *We have 40 bits. How many skinnies are 40 bits? What is 40×2?*

Note $40 \times 2 = 80$, which is 8 skinnies or 80 bits.

Pose another problem. Ask:

- *What if we had 70 bits? What value of* n *makes $3 \times 70 = $ n true?*

Note 70 bits is 7 skinnies so 3×7 skinnies is 21 skinnies or 210. The amount 210 can be thought of as 210 bits, 21 skinnies, or 2 flats and 1 skinny.

Discuss patterns in multiplying by multiples of ten. Write the following problems on the blackboard or overhead projector. Ask students to fill in the answers and look for patterns. Tell children to imagine groups of base-ten pieces as they do the problems. For example, 3×1000 can be thought of as 3 packs, 3 groups of 10 flats, 3 groups of 100 skinnies, or 3 groups of 1000 bits. Students can use calculators.

$3 \times 1 = $ _____ $3 \times 2 = $ _____

$3 \times 10 = $ _____ $3 \times 20 = $ _____

$3 \times 100 = $ _____ $3 \times 200 = $ _____

$3 \times 1000 = $ _____ $3 \times 2000 = $ _____

$3 \times 10,000 = $ _____ $3 \times 20,000 = $ _____

Remind students that 10, 100, 1000, etc., as well as 20, 200, 2000, etc., are all **multiples** of 10. Ask students to try the next problems without their calculators. Refer them to the problems they just completed. Students will soon see that the problem is really how many zeros are at the end of the product. They can use calculators if needed. Write the problems listed below on the board or overhead along with additional

TIMS Tip

Most likely, you will not have enough bits or unit cubes for everyone to do these problems. You may have to combine groups or use dots on paper as shorthand. Also, it is fine for children to imagine that they have more pieces than they actually do have. This helps children move from the concrete to the abstract.

Multiplying by 10s

On Monday, ten of the candy machines at the TIMS Candy Company were working. Each machine can make four Chocos in one minute. On Monday, how many Chocos were made every minute at the company?

A number sentence for this question is $4 + 4 + 4 + 4 + 4 + 4 + 4 + 4 + 4 + 4 = n$.

Another way to write this is $10 \times 4 = n$. What number must n be to make the sentences true?

The value of n is 40 (or $n = 40$) since 40 is 10 groups of 4.

$4 + 4 + 4 + 4 + 4 + 4 + 4 + 4 + 4 + 4 = 40$ and $10 \times 4 = 40$.

We can also say this as $4 \times 10 = 40$. This is the same as 4 groups of 10.

Complete Questions 1 and 2. You may use your calculator.

1. There are 10 polar bears at the Greenville Zoo. Each bear eats 6 pounds of fish a day. How many pounds of fish are eaten by polar bears at the Greenville Zoo every day? Write an addition sentence for this problem and solve. Write a multiplication sentence for the problem and solve.

Student Guide - Page 193

2. Tanya has 10 friends who wrote her letters when she was away at camp. Each friend wrote Tanya 3 letters. How many letters did Tanya receive? Draw a picture of the problem and write a multiplication sentence.

3. Luis says that multiplication by multiples of 10 is easy.
   A. Do the following problems. You may use your calculator if necessary.

10	20	40	30	70	40	80	20	90
×6	×3	×3	×7	×2	×6	×2	×9	×8

   B. Do you notice a pattern in multiplying by multiples of 10? Describe it.

4. Do the following problems. You may use your multiplication table.

60	70	40	20	50	50	90
×4	×5	×7	×2	×6	×5	×3

5. Frank said one of the problems in Question 4 was tricky. He almost got it wrong. Which one do you think Frank is talking about and why is it tricky?

6. Irma found some more patterns on her calculator. Describe the patterns.

   $7 \times 1 = 7$ $7 \times 4 = 28$
   $7 \times 10 = 70$ $7 \times 40 = 280$
   $7 \times 100 = 700$ $7 \times 400 = 2800$
   $7 \times 1000 = 7000$ $7 \times 4000 = 28,000$
   $7 \times 10,000 = 70,000$ $7 \times 40000 = 280,000$

7. Find the products. You may use a calculator if necessary.
   A. $6 \times 1 =$
       $6 \times 10 =$
       $6 \times 100 =$
       $6 \times 1000 =$
       $6 \times 10,000 =$
   B. $6 \times 3 =$
       $6 \times 30 =$
       $6 \times 300 =$
       $6 \times 3000 =$
       $6 \times 30,000 =$
   C. $6 \times 5 =$
       $6 \times 50 =$
       $6 \times 500 =$
       $6 \times 5000 =$
       $6 \times 50,000 =$

Student Guide - Page 194

practice problems that are similar. Encourage students to use their multiplication tables if they wish.

$$6 \times 20 \qquad 30 \times 6 \qquad 4 \times 400$$
$$40 \times 6 \qquad 2 \times 700 \qquad 9 \times 600 \qquad 6 \times 500$$

Ask:

- *Do you need to use calculators for these problems? Is there a quicker way?*

Someone should notice that in order to solve the problem, students need to use their multiplication facts and then count the number of zeros.

Make sure you discuss the problem 6×500 with the class. In this problem, the answer has 3 zeros, not 2 zeros. This is because $6 \times 5 = 30$. Remind students to be careful when counting zeros.

Students can investigate what happens when two multidigit numbers that end in zero are multiplied (e.g., $50 \times 30, 400 \times 60$). Encourage students to continue to explore patterns in these types of problems. Lesson 7 of this unit further investigates multiples of ten.

Once students have identified the pattern to multiplying by multiples of ten, provide further practice with number sentences that include unknowns and multiples of ten. Put the following problems on the board or overhead. Ask students to find what n is in the following problems. Note that n can stand for a missing factor as well as a missing product.

$$3 \times 70 = n \qquad 60 \times 3 = n \qquad 9 \times 500 = n$$
$$4 \times n = 800 \qquad 3 \times n = 6000 \qquad 5 \times n = 1500$$
$$n \times 4000 = 24,000 \quad n \times 70 = 420 \quad n \times 8000 = 56,000$$

Have several students explain how they found n. Do more examples like this as necessary.

Students should read *Multiplying by 10s* in the *Student Guide* and do **Questions 1–10** in class. Review the problems together.

 Journal Prompt

Why can multiplication problems be "turned around"? Can addition problems be turned around? How about subtraction problems? What about division problems? Explain.

Suggestions for Teaching the Lesson

Math Facts

DPP items M, N, and O practice multiplication strategies using doubling, breaking apart numbers, and numbers ending in zeros.

Homework and Practice

Assign the Homework section in the *Student Guide*. Students will need calculators to check work.

Assessment

Use Part 5 of the Home Practice as a quiz.

Answers for Part 5 of the Home Practice can be found in the Answer Key at the end of this lesson and at the end of this unit.

Extension

DPP item P provides a challenging problem involving multiples, factors, and divisibility rules.

---

8. For the following problems, make a prediction of what you think the answer will be. Then, do the problem on your calculator to check.
   A. 8×30 B. 40×5 C. 200×3 D. 5×600
   E. 7×2000 F. 90×4 G. 600×2

9. Predict what number *n* must be to make the number sentence true. Check your work on a calculator.
   A. $200 \times 5 = n$ B. $60 \times n = 120$ C. $5000 \times n = 15,000$
   D. $n \times 40 = 80$ E. $n \times 700 = 4900$ F. $6 \times n = 6000$
   G. $n \times 6 = 3600$ H. $2 \times n = 1400$

10. Can you find a rule that makes multiplying numbers that end in zeros easy?

Homework

For the following problems, make a prediction of what you think the answer will be. Then, do the problem on your calculator to check.

1. 8×3	2. 9×6	3. 7×6
8×30	9×60	7×60
8×300	9×600	7×600
8×3000	9×6000	7×6000
$8 \times 30,000$	$9 \times 60,000$	$7 \times 60,000$

4. $30 \times 7 = n$

5. $500 \times 8 = n$

6. $300 \times 9 = n$

7. $7 \times 200 = n$

8. $4 \times 6000 = n$

9. 3000 10. 5000 11. 100 12. 400 13. 600
    $\times 4$ $\times 7$ $\times 9$ $\times 3$ $\times 2$

Multiplying by 10s   SG · Grade 4 · Unit 7 · Lesson 4 195

Student Guide - Page 195

Daily Practice and Problems: Task and Challenge for Lesson 4

N. Task: Break Apart Eights
(URG p. 17)

One way to solve 6×8 is to break the 8 into $5 + 3$.

$6 \times 5 = 30$ $6 \times 3 = 18$

6

5   3

$6 \times 8 = 30 + 18 = 48$

$6 \times 5 = 30$ and $6 \times 3 = 18$, so
$6 \times 8 = 30 + 18 = 48$

1. Draw a picture for 6×8 that uses 8 broken into $7 + 1$.

2. Find another way to break up 8. Draw a picture. Write a number sentence for this picture.

3. Write the four number sentences in the fact family for 6×8.

P. Challenge: Basketball Teams **N**
(URG p. 18)

The local park district sponsors a basketball league. The coaches divide the children into three divisions of equal size. Individual teams are made up of five children. The winning team goes to the state finals. If the league must have more than 100 children, but less than 150, what number of children can form three divisions with teams of five members in each division?

14. A zoo has 10 displays of turtles. Each display has 4 turtles. How many turtles are at the zoo? Draw a picture. Write an addition sentence and a multiplication sentence. Solve.

15. There are 10 elevators in an office building. There can be up to 9 people in an elevator at one time. How many people can ride the elevators at the same time?

16. There are 3 juice boxes in a juice pack. If Roberto's mother buys 10 juice packs, how many juice boxes is that?

17. A juice pack costs $2.00. How much will 8 juice packs cost? How much will 10 juice packs cost?

18. There are 30 desks in every fourth-grade classroom at Holmes School. If there are 5 fourth-grade classes, how many desks are there for fourth graders?

19. There are 8 granola bars in a package. A school buys 40 packages. How many granola bars is that?

20. A large bottle of ketchup costs $3.00. The head cook at Stanley School buys 40 bottles. How much money does he spend on ketchup?

Predict what number _n_ must be to make the number sentence true. Check your work on a calculator.

21. $200 \times n = 600$	22. $n \times 2 = 800$	23. $2 \times n = 600$
24. $2 \times n = 20,000$	25. $n \times 7000 = 42,000$	26. $n \times 800 = 3200$
27. $60 \times 7 = n$	28. $n \times 8 = 320$	29. $n \times 400 = 2800$

Multiplying by 10s

Suggestions for Teaching the Lesson (_continued_)

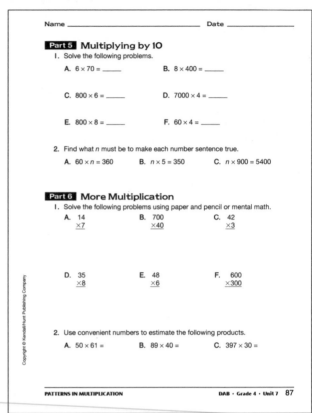

Name _____ Date _____

Part 5 Multiplying by 10

1. Solve the following problems.

A. $6 \times 70 =$ _____   B. $8 \times 400 =$ _____

C. $800 \times 6 =$ _____   D. $7000 \times 4 =$ _____

E. $800 \times 8 =$ _____   F. $60 \times 4 =$ _____

2. Find what _n_ must be to make each number sentence true.

A. $60 \times n = 360$ B. $n \times 5 = 350$ C. $n \times 900 = 5400$

Part 6 More Multiplication

1. Solve the following problems using paper and pencil or mental math.

A. 14   B. 700   C. 42
   $\times 7$ $\times 40$ $\times 3$

D. 35   E. 48   F. 600
   $\times 8$ $\times 6$ $\times 300$

2. Use convenient numbers to estimate the following products.

A. $50 \times 61 =$ B. $89 \times 40 =$ C. $397 \times 30 =$

Copyright © Kendall/Hunt Publishing Company

PATTERNS IN MULTIPLICATION   **DAB · Grade 4 · Unit 7** 87

AT A GLANCE

Math Facts and Daily Practice and Problems

DPP items M, N, and O practice math facts strategies for the last six facts. Challenge P uses multiples, factors, and divisibility rules.

Developing the Activity

1. Introduce multiplying one-digit numbers by 10 with base-ten pieces.
2. Remind students of the use of an unknown in a number sentence.
3. Multiply one-digit numbers by multiples of 10 with base-ten pieces.
4. Discuss turn-around facts.
5. Investigate multiplication sentences involving multiples of 100, 1000, and 10,000.
6. Students solve problems with an unknown as a missing product as well as a missing factor.
7. Assign students _Questions 1–10_ on the _Multiplying by 10s_ Activity Pages in the _Student Guide_. Discuss them as a class.

Homework

Assign the Homework section in the _Student Guide_.

Assessment

Use Home Practice Part 5 as a quiz.

Notes:

Student Guide

Questions 1–10 (SG pp. 193–195)

1. 60 pounds; Number sentences will vary. 6 + 6 + 6 + 6 + 6 + 6 + 6 + 6 + 6 + 6 = 60; 10 × 6 = 60

2. 30 letters; Number sentences will vary. 3 + 3 + 3 + 3 + 3 + 3 + 3 + 3 + 3 + 3 = 30

3. **A.** 60; 60; 120; 210; 140; 240; 160; 180; 720
   B. The product for the multiplication fact is followed by a zero.

4. 240; 350; 280; 40; 300; 250; 270

5. 50 × 6; the answer has two zeros not one. This is because 6 × 5 is 30.

6. The number of zeros in the product equals the number of zeros in the problem.

7. **A.** 6; 60; 600; 6000; 60,000
   B. 18; 180; 1800; 18,000; 180,000
   C. 30; 300; 3000; 30,000; 300,000

8. **A.** 240   **B.** 200
   C. 600   **D.** 3000
   E. 14,000   **F.** 360
   G. 1200

9. **A.** 1000   **B.** 2
   C. 3   **D.** 2
   E. 7   **F.** 1000
   G. 600   **H.** 700

10. Answers will vary. Do the multiplication fact, then count up the zeros in the problem and add the same number at the end of the fact solution.

Homework (SG pp. 195–196)

Questions 1–29

1. 24; 240; 2400; 24,000; 240,000
2. 54; 540; 5400; 54,000; 540,000
3. 42; 420; 4200; 42,000; 420,000
4. 210
5. 4000
6. 2700
7. 1400
8. 24,000
9. 12,000
10. 35,000
11. 900
12. 1200
13. 1200
14. 40 turtles; 10 × 4 = 40; 4 + 4 + 4 + 4 + 4 + 4 + 4 + 4 + 4 + 4 = 40
15. 90 people
16. 30 juice boxes
17. $16; $20
18. 150 desks
19. 320 granola bars
20. $120
21. 3
22. 400
23. 300
24. 10,000
25. 6
26. 4
27. 420
28. 40
29. 7

Discovery Assignment Book

** Home Practice (DAB p. 87)

Part 5. Multiplying by 10

Questions 1–2

1. **A.** 420
   B. 3200
   C. 4800
   D. 28,000
   E. 6400
   F. 240

2. **A.** 6
   B. 70
   C. 6

*Answers and/or discussion are included in the Lesson Guide.

**Answers for all the Home Practice in the *Discovery Assignment Book* are at the end of the unit.

Q. Division by 10 (URG p. 18)

You may use a calculator to divide.

A. $20 \div 10 =$ B. $70 \div 10 =$

C. $100 \div 10 =$ D. $50 \div 10 =$

E. $120 \div 10 =$ F. $180 \div 10 =$

What pattern do you see? How can this pattern help you estimate the answers to the following problems?

$136 \div 10 =$ $178 \div 10 =$ $235 \div 10 =$

S. Multiplication Times Two
   (URG p. 19)

Solve the problems two ways. Use both paper and pencil and mental math. Be prepared to explain your mental math strategies.

1. 79×3

2. 52×6

U. Finding Means (URG p. 21)

Here is Jackie's data for a paper towel experiment. She dropped water on one sheet of three different brands of paper towels. She dropped three drops of water on each towel. The water spread out and made a spot. Jackie measured the area of each spot in square centimeters.

T Type of Towel	A Area (in sq cm)			
	Trial 1	Trial 2	Trial 3	Mean
Ecotowel	23 sq cm	20 sq cm	21 sq cm	
Cheap-O	37 sq cm	36 sq cm	41 sq cm	
Handy	11 sq cm	10 sq cm	12 sq cm	

Use a calculator to find the mean area for each type of towel. Give your answer to the nearest cm.

DPP Tasks and Challenge are on page 75.
Suggestions for using the DPPs are on page 75.

LESSON GUIDE 5
Multiplication

Estimated
Class
Sessions:
3–4

Students are introduced to a paper and pencil multiplication algorithm. This method, called the all-partials method, records all partial products.

Key Content

- Representing multiplication using base-ten pieces.
- Multiplying 1-digit by 2-digit numbers using paper and pencil.

Key Vocabulary

all-partials method of multiplication

Curriculum Sequence

Before This Unit

Multiplication. In Grade 3 Unit 19, students break apart products into the sum of simpler products, e.g., $6 \times 8 = 6 \times 5 + 6 \times 3$. They begin with one-digit by one-digit problems and move to two-digit by one-digit problems. To do this, students use rectangular arrays and multiplication stories.

After This Unit

Multiplication. Students will study multiplication algorithms in Unit 11.

Materials List

Print Materials for Students

		Math Facts and Daily Practice and Problems	Activity	Homework
Student Book	**Student Guide**		*Multiplication* Pages 197–199	*Multiplication* Homework Section Pages 199–201
Teacher Resources	**Unit Resource Guide**	DPP Items Q–V Pages 18–21		
	Generic Section		*Base-Ten Board Parts 1* and *2,* 1 per student pair, *Recording Sheet,* 1 per student plus extras, and *Small Multiplication Tables* or completed *Multiplication Facts I Know* charts, 1 per student	

available on Teacher Resource CD

All Transparency Masters, Blackline Masters, and Assessment Blackline Masters in the Unit Resource Guide are on the Teacher Resource CD.

Supplies for Each Student Pair

set of base-ten pieces

Materials for the Teacher

Transparency of *Base-Ten Board Part 1* Blackline Master (Unit Resource Guide, Generic Section)
Transparency of *Recording Sheet* Blackline Master (Unit Resource Guide, Generic Section)
Observational Assessment Record (Unit Resource Guide, Pages 7–8 and Teacher Resource CD)
overhead base-ten pieces, optional

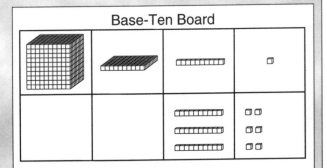

Figure 11: *3 groups of 12*

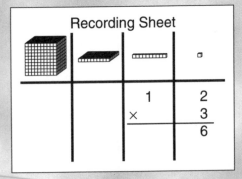

Figure 12: *Beginning the problem:*
2 × 3 = 6

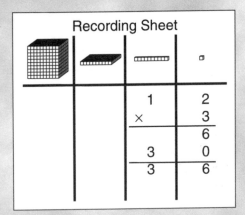

Figure 13: *3 × 10 = 30,*
30 + 6 = 36

⏱IMS Tip

When your students have a good understanding of the place value columns, you can use the *Recording Sheet* occasionally to remind students of the columns. Otherwise, the *Recording Sheet* can be abandoned. Teachers often ask their students to use graph paper for paper and pencil calculations as a reminder to keep the columns lined up correctly.

Developing the Activity

Begin this lesson as a class discussion. Ask students:

- *Joe, a worker at the TIMS Candy Company, makes 12 pieces of candy each minute. How much candy does he make in 3 minutes?*

Discuss with the class the various ways of solving this problem. The class may suggest adding 12 + 12 + 12 or breaking 12 apart into 10 + 2 and writing 3 × 10 + 3 × 2. We will look at this problem on the *Base-Ten Board*.

First, model the problem with base-ten pieces on the board or overhead as shown in Figure 11.

We have 3 groups of 2 bits, which gives 6 bits. Write this on the *Recording Sheet* as shown in Figure 12. Note the 6 is written in the bits' column.

In the skinnies' column, we see there are 3 groups of 1 skinny, making 3 skinnies, so we write 3 in the skinnies' column and 0 in the bits' column. Note to the class that 3 skinnies is the same as 30 bits. See Figure 13.

Thus, we have a total of 3 skinnies and 6 bits (or 36 bits). This method of writing out all the partial products while multiplying is called the **all-partials method** (or algorithm). The traditional multiplication algorithm is very similar to the all-partials method, but abbreviates the recordings.

- *For 4 minutes in a row, Joe made 23 pieces of candy. How much candy did he make altogether?*

He recorded this as 2 skinnies and 3 bits four times. See Figure 14.

Base-Ten Board

Figure 14: *2 skinnies and 3 bits four times*

First we look at the bits. There are 4 groups of 3 bits which makes 12 bits, as shown in Figure 15. We can exchange 10 bits to make 1 skinny and 2 bits. Note that writing the number of bits (12) and writing bits and skinnies (12) is the same. The base-ten system automatically records 12 as 1 skinny and 2 bits. Show the first partial product with the *Recording Sheet*.

In the skinnies' column, we have 4 groups of 2 skinnies which makes 8 skinnies and 0 bits (or 80 bits). In total we have 9 skinnies and 2 bits.

The first *Recording Sheet* in Figure 16 shows 23 × 4 solved starting from the right as described above. The *Recording Sheet* on the bottom shows the problem solved starting from the left. Starting the all-partials method from the left is appropriate since students often use front-end estimation to estimate the answer to a multiplication problem (e.g., 4 × 23 is about 80). On the other hand, starting the problem from the right provides an easier transition to the compact or traditional algorithm. Either method (starting with the right or starting with the left) works when using the all-partials method. The traditional algorithm is introduced in Unit 11.

As another example, set up 52 × 6 on the *Base-Ten Board* (Use 6 groups of 5 skinnies and 2 bits). The 6 groups of 2 bits gives 12 bits or 1 skinny and 2 bits. Write either on the *Recording Sheet* or on the blackboard as in Figure 17.

$$\begin{array}{r} 52 \\ \times\ 6 \\ \hline 12 \end{array}$$

Figure 17: *Beginning the problem 6 × 52*

Now we see that 6 groups of 5 skinnies gives 30 skinnies or 3 flats, 0 skinnies, and 0 bits (or 300 bits). We write these in the appropriate columns. See Figure 18.

$$\begin{array}{r} 52 \\ \times\ 6 \\ \hline 12 \\ 300 \\ \hline 312 \end{array}$$

Figure 18: *6 × 2 = 12, 6 × 50 = 300, 300 + 12 = 312*

Have the class practice several more problems such as these:

15 × 6	32 × 3	34 × 4
53 × 4	65 × 3	95 × 6

Students should model the problem on their *Base-Ten Boards*. Then, they should compute the answer using the all-partials method. Some students may need to use their multiplication tables.

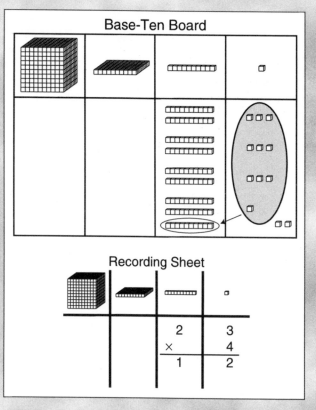

Figure 15: *Beginning the problem 4 × 23*

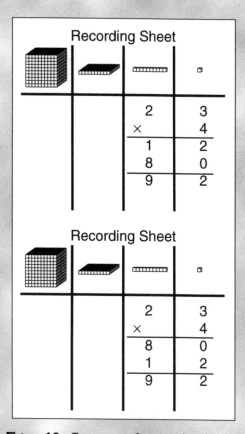

Figure 16: *Two ways of computing 4 × 23*

Student Guide - Page 197

Multiplication

Mrs. Haddad noticed that 4 of the workers at the TIMS Candy Company each made 32 Chocos in one hour. To find the total number of Chocos made, Mrs. Haddad used base-ten pieces and wrote 32 + 32 + 32 + 32. She said this could be an addition problem or a multiplication problem.

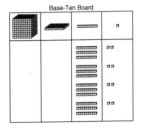

Mrs. Haddad used the **all-partials method** to solve the problem by multiplication. Since there are 4 groups of 2 bits, there are 8 bits total.

$$\begin{array}{r} 3\ 2 \\ \times\ \ 4 \\ \hline 8 \end{array}$$

Since there are 4 groups of 3 skinnies, this makes 12 skinnies or 1 flat, 2 skinnies, and 0 bits or 120 bits. The workers made a total of 128 Chocos in 1 hour.

$$\begin{array}{r} 3\ 2 \\ \times\ \ 4 \\ \hline 8 \\ 1\ 2\ 0 \\ \hline 1\ 2\ 8 \end{array}$$

Multiplication   SG · Grade 4 · Unit 7 · Lesson 5 **197**

Student Guide - Page 197

Student Guide - Page 198

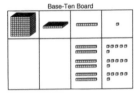

One of the employees at the TIMS Candy Company solved the problem a little differently. His work is shown here. He first found that 4 groups of 3 skinnies makes 120 bits. Then, he found that 4 groups of 2 bits makes 8 bits total. The answer matches Mrs. Haddad's answer—128 Chocos.

$$\begin{array}{r} 3\ 2 \\ \times\ \ 4 \\ \hline 1\ 2\ 0 \\ 8 \\ \hline 1\ 2\ 8 \end{array}$$

1. On another day, 3 workers at the TIMS Candy Company each made 26 pieces of candy in one hour.

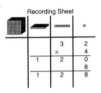

A. Fill in the missing numbers. Since there are 3 groups of 6 bits, there are ____ bits or ____ skinny and ____ bits.
We write this as shown on the *Recording Sheet* to the right.

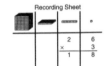

$$\begin{array}{r} 2\ 6 \\ \times\ \ 3 \\ \hline 1\ \ 8 \end{array}$$

198 SG · Grade 4 · Unit 7 · Lesson 5   Multiplication

Student Guide - Page 198

Student Guide - Page 199

B. Since there are 3 groups of 2 skinnies, there are ____ skinnies. This is the same as ____ skinnies and ____ bits.
We write this as shown on the *Recording Sheet* to the right.

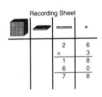

$$\begin{array}{r} 2\ 6 \\ \times\ \ 3 \\ \hline 1\ \ 8 \\ 6\ 0 \\ \hline 7\ 8 \end{array}$$

C. What is the total number of candies made by the workers at the TIMS Candy Company?

Use base-ten pieces and the all-partials method to do the following problems:

2. 12
   ×3

3. 61
   ×4

4. 26
   ×4

5. 57
   ×4

6. 83
   ×9

Homework

Solve the following problems. You may use your multiplication table. You may also check your work on a calculator.

1. 20   50   90   60   40   70   80
   ×8   ×3   ×4   ×7   ×9   ×6   ×6

2. 100   30,000   700   200   40,000   700
   ×5   ×7   ×5   ×4   ×6   ×8

3. Find *n* for each of the problems.

   A. $5 \times 60 = n$
   B. $70 \times 2 = n$
   C. $n = 3 \times 600$
   D. $n = 100 \times 5$
   E. $n \times 70 = 140$
   F. $500 \times n = 4000$
   G. $80 = n \times 20$
   H. $700 = 7 \times n$
   I. $7 \times 800 = n$

Multiplication   SG · Grade 4 · Unit 7 · Lesson 5 **199**

Student Guide - Page 199

Student Guide - Page 200

Write a number sentence for each problem and solve. You may also want to draw a picture.

4. A sailboat can travel about 30 miles in 1 hour. How far can the sailboat travel in 6 hours?

5. There are about 50 crackers in a box. If 5 children share the box, how many crackers does each child get?

6. Mr. Thoms drove for 3 hours without stopping. He drove about 50 miles every hour (50 miles per hour or 50 mph). About how far did he drive?

Fill in the missing numbers in the multiplication problems. You may use base-ten shorthand if it is helpful. You may also use your multiplication table.

7. 13   8. 42   9. 51
   ×7   ×6   ×4
   21   ◯   4
   70   240   ◯
   ◯   252   204
   252

10. Solve the problems. You may use base-ten shorthand if it is helpful. You may also use your multiplication tables.

    A. 14   B. 21   C. 52   D. 25   E. 41
       ×2   ×6   ×3   ×3   ×6

    F. 65   G. 83   H. 76   I. 78   J. 67
       ×6   ×7   ×9   ×6   ×4

11. There are 32 students in Miguel's class. For his birthday, Miguel's mother baked cookies to bring to school. If he wanted to give each student 4 cookies, how many cookies must his mother bake?

12. At Livingston School there are 3 fourth-grade classes. If there are 26 students in each class, how many fourth graders are there at Livingston School?

200 SG · Grade 4 · Unit 7 · Lesson 5   Multiplication

Student Guide - Page 200

Suggestions for Teaching the Lesson

Homework and Practice

- Assign parts of the Homework section in the *Student Guide* as students work on the lesson. Since students will not have base-ten pieces at home, remind them how to use base-ten shorthand to help them solve the multiplication problems. Encourage students to use their multiplication tables as needed.

- DPP Bit Q practices dividing by 10. Bit S provides practice with multiplication. Task T practices rounding with number lines. Bit U provides practice finding the mean. Task V practices strategies for adding and subtracting using mental math.

Assessment

Use the *Observational Assessment Record* to document students' abilities to multiply numbers with ending zeros and to multiply 1-digit by 2-digit numbers using paper and pencil.

Extension

DPP item R provides a challenging problem involving money.

---

13. A zoo has 22 lions. Each lion eats 8 pounds of meat a day. How much meat must the zookeeper bring to the lion exhibit each day?

14. The Rodriguez family is having a big party. Mrs. Rodriguez knows she should have 70 cans of soda. Ana buys 3 cases of soda. Each case contains 24 cans of soda. Will this be enough soda? Why or why not?

15. The array below has 6 rows of 13 tiles. How many tiles are in the array?

16. An array has 7 rows of 46 tiles. How many tiles in all are in the array?

17. An array has 9 rows of 58 tiles. How many tiles in all are in the array?

18. An array has 7 rows of 99 tiles. How many tiles? Explain a way to do this problem in your head.

Multiplication   SG · Grade 4 · Unit 7 · Lesson 5 201

Student Guide - Page 201

Daily Practice and Problems: Tasks and Challenge for Lesson 5

R. Challenge: Seventeen Cents (URG p. 19)

If you have three nickels and two pennies, then you have 17¢. You can show this by writing: $3 \times 5¢ + 2 \times 1¢ = 17¢$.

1. Find all the different combinations of coins that make 17¢. You may use pennies, nickels, and dimes.

2. Write number sentences to show coins that make 17¢.

3. Explain how you know you found all the combinations.

T. Task: Big Numbers (URG p. 20)

Draw the number line below.

400,000   500,000

1. Make a mark on the line to show 478,923.

2. Round 478,923 to the nearest 100,000.

3. Round 478,923 to the nearest 10,000. What benchmarks did you use? Add these benchmarks to the number line.

4. Round 323,701 to the nearest 100,000. Draw a number line that includes this number and label the number line with benchmarks. Make a mark for 323,701.

5. Round 323,701 to the nearest 10,000. What benchmarks did you use? Add these benchmarks to your number line.

V. Task: Adding and Subtracting for Practice (URG p. 21)

Do the following problems mentally. Be ready to explain how you solved each problem without paper and pencil.

A. 89,300   B. 77,900   C. 65,800
   −   102   + 1100   − 5099

Use paper and pencil to solve problems D–F. Use estimation to help you decide if your answers make sense.

D. 13,457   E. 85,609   F. 67,890
   − 4294   − 6725   + 32,484

AT A GLANCE

Math Facts and Daily Practice and Problems

DPP item Q practices dividing by 10. Challenge R involves problem solving with money. Item S practices multiplication. Task T develops number sense using number lines. Item U practices finding means. Task V practices strategies for adding and subtracting.

Developing the Activity

1. Model multiplying two-digit by one-digit numbers using base-ten pieces and how to record the process on *Recording Sheets*.
2. Introduce the all-partials method of multiplication and relate it to the base-ten pieces.
3. Do the *Multiplication* Activity Pages in the *Student Guide* in groups and then discuss as a class.

Homework

Assign the Homework section on the *Multiplication* Activity Pages.

Assessment

Use the *Observational Assessment Record* to document students' progress with multiplication.

Notes:

Student Guide

Questions 1–6 (SG pp. 198–199)

I. A. 18 bits; 1 skinny and 8 bits

B. 6 skinnies; 6 skinnies and 0 bits

C. 78 Chocos

2. 36
$$
\begin{array}{r}
12 \\
\times\ 3 \\
\hline
6 \\
30 \\
\hline
36
\end{array}
$$

3. 244
$$
\begin{array}{r}
61 \\
\times\ 4 \\
\hline
4 \\
240 \\
\hline
244
\end{array}
$$

4. 104
$$
\begin{array}{r}
26 \\
\times\ 4 \\
\hline
24 \\
80 \\
\hline
104
\end{array}
$$

5. 228
$$
\begin{array}{r}
57 \\
\times\ 4 \\
\hline
28 \\
200 \\
\hline
228
\end{array}
$$

6. 747
$$
\begin{array}{r}
83 \\
\times\ 9 \\
\hline
27 \\
720 \\
\hline
747
\end{array}
$$

Homework (SG pp. 199–201)

Questions 1–18

I. 160; 150; 360; 420; 360; 420; 480

2. 500; 210,000; 3500; 800; 240,000; 5600

3. A. 300

B. 140

C. 1800

D. 500

E. 2

F. 8

G. 4

H. 100

I. 5600

4. 180 miles; $30 \times 6 = 180$

5. 10 crackers; $10 \times 5 = 50$

6. 150 miles; $50 \times 3 = 150$

7. 91

8. 12

9. 200

10. A. 28

B. 126

C. 156

D. 75

E. 246

F. 390

G. 581

H. 684

I. 468

J. 268

II. 128 cookies

12. 78 fourth graders

13. 176 pounds

14. Yes; $24 \times 3 = 72$ cans

15. 78 tiles

16. 322 tiles

17. 522 tiles

18. 693 tiles; Explanations will vary.
Students might multiply $7 \times 100 = 700$,
then subtract 7 to get 693.

*Answers and/or discussion are included in the Lesson Guide.

**Answers for all the Home Practice in the *Discovery Assignment Book* are at the end of the unit.

Daily Practice and Problems:
Bits for Lesson 6

W. Oceans (URG p. 22)

1. The Pacific Ocean covers 64,186,300 square miles. The Atlantic Ocean covers 33,420,000 square miles. About how many more square miles does the Pacific Ocean cover than the Atlantic?

2. The Indian Ocean covers 28,350,000 square miles. Do the Atlantic and Indian Oceans combined cover more or less area than the Pacific Ocean?

Y. Multiplying by Multiples of 10
(URG p. 22)

A. $600 \times 4 =$ B. $8000 \times 7 =$

C. $4 \times 70 =$ D. $800 \times 6 =$

E. $8 \times 4000 =$ F. $600 \times 7 =$

DPP Task and Challenge are on page 82.
Suggestions for using the DPPs are on pages 82–83.

LESSON GUIDE 6
Estimation

| Estimated Class Sessions: **2** | Students develop strategies for computational estimation for multiplication. Students explore situations where estimates are appropriate and make estimates using convenient numbers. |

Key Content

* Choosing to find an estimate or an exact answer.
* Choosing convenient numbers.
* Estimating sums, differences, and products.

Key Vocabulary

convenient numbers
estimation

Curriculum Sequence

Before This Unit

Estimation. In Unit 1 Lesson 6, students discuss when it is appropriate to calculate with paper and pencil, find an estimate, or use a calculator. In Unit 3, students use front-end estimation to estimate the answers to addition and subtraction problems using base-ten pieces as a reference. They use estimation when checking the reasonableness of their answers. In Unit 6 Lesson 6, students use number lines to round big numbers and to identify benchmarks that can be used when rounding numbers. Round numbers are used in estimating sums and differences of large numbers. For more information about estimation, refer to the TIMS Tutors: *Estimation, Accuracy, and Error* and *Arithmetic* in the *Teacher Implementation Guide.*

After This Unit

Estimation. Throughout fourth grade, students will continue to choose the appropriate method of computation (estimation, paper-and-pencil, or calculator) for a given situation. They will also use estimation to check the reasonableness of their results. See especially Units 11 and 13.

Materials List

Print Materials for Students

	Math Facts and Daily Practice and Problems	Activity	Homework	Written Assessment
Student Book — Student Guide		*Estimation* Pages 202–205	*Estimation* Homework Section Pages 205–206	
Teacher Resources — Facts Resource Guide	DPP Item 7Y			
Teacher Resources — Unit Resource Guide	DPP Items W–Z Pages 22–23			DPP Item Y *Multiplying by Multiples of 10,* Page 22

available on Teacher Resource CD

All Transparency Masters, Blackline Masters, and Assessment Blackline Masters in the Unit Resource Guide are on the Teacher Resource CD.

Materials for the Teacher

Observational Assessment Record (Unit Resource Guide, Pages 7–8 and Teacher Resource CD)

Developing the Activity

Part 1. Estimating with Multiplication

Oftentimes, we cannot or do not need to find exact answers. In these cases, an estimate is good enough. Remind students that the word **estimate** means "about how much." "Estimate" can be used as a noun or a verb. We "estimate" the number of people at a ball game to get an "estimate."

Discuss the following questions that involve money and estimating. In real life, we must always consider sales tax when discussing purchasing items. You can say that for now you will not consider sales tax or say "plus some more for tax" in answering money problems. If your students are comfortable with finding 10 percent, this can be added to the first estimate to arrive at a safe, final estimate.

- *If 1 apple costs 18¢, about how much do 3 apples cost?* (We can round 18¢ to 20¢. Then $3 \times 20¢ = 60¢$. Students may also round to 15¢. Since $3 \times 15¢ = 45¢$, we know that the cost is between 45¢ and 60¢.)

- *Shirts cost $19.50. If you buy 4 shirts, about how much money will you spend?* (Students can round $19.50 to $20.00. $4 \times \$20.00 = \$80.00$.)

- *A bag of cat litter is $3.67. About how much will 2 bags cost?* (Answers will vary depending on the rounding. Students can estimate that the cost is between $2 \times \$3.50$ and $2 \times \$4$ or between $7 and $8.)

Next, have students read the introduction on the *Estimation* Activity Pages in the *Student Guide*. Nicholas and Lee Yah use different convenient numbers to estimate the answer to 5.79×2. Use this example to emphasize that estimates will vary from student to student. Some students might suggest rounding $5.79 to other convenient numbers such as $5, $5.50, or $5.75 rather than the $6.00 used by Nicholas. If we used these numbers, however, we would be underestimating. Nicholas might think he has enough money, but in reality he is short. It is better to overestimate in situations like this one.

Discuss *Questions 1–7* in groups and then as a class. In *Question 3,* to estimate the answer to 47×4, students might round 47 to 50 and get an estimate of $200. Others might use front-end estimation and use the convenient number 40. These students would get an estimate of $160. Discuss which estimate is more appropriate. In this case, overestimating will give Mrs. Borko a better idea of whether or not she has enough money to pay for 4 jackets.

Content Note

Good Estimates and Ten Percent. We often use 10% as a standard for determining when a prediction is good, i.e., when it is "close" to the actual result. (See the optional lesson in Unit 6 Lesson 5.) There are many situations, however, where 10% is not appropriate. In particular, it is not a good idea to use 10% as a measure of "goodness" for a computational estimation. In particular, when we estimate the result of a multiplication problem, a good estimate will often not be within 10% of the actual result. For example, if we estimate 23×22 by rounding off each factor we get an estimate of 400, which is reasonable by any standard. But this cannot possibly be within 10% since rounding 23 to 20 is already a decrease of about 15%, and rounding 22 to 20 is another decrease by 10%. Now 23×22 is 506, so our estimate is low by over 20%. Still it's a good estimate. In **most** cases we probably do not want to bother figuring out how close a computational estimate is. In the time it takes to figure this out, you could probably do the computation exactly.

Estimation

Nicholas wants to buy two books that each cost $5.79. He **estimates** the cost of the two books to get a good idea of how much he will have to spend. In order to find the estimate, Nicholas uses a **convenient number.** He thinks, "$5.79 is close to $6.00 but $6.00 is easier to work with than $5.79." He multiplies $2 \times \$6$ in his head and comes up with an estimate of $12.00.

As Nicholas waited in line at the cashier, he shared his estimate with Lee Yah. She estimated the total too and then said, "Your estimate is close to mine. I doubled $5.80. I knew $2 \times \$5$ is $10 and $2 \times 80¢ = \$1.60$. My estimate is $11.60."

Nicholas chose the number 6 when estimating because it was a convenient number to work with in his head. He rounded $5.79 to the nearest whole dollar, $6. Rounded numbers are one type of convenient number. Lee Yah chose the convenient number $5.80 because she could double $5.80 in her head more easily than $5.79. Remember, a number that is convenient for one person might not be convenient for another.

1. A. Keenya has a bag of 25 oatmeal cookies to share with her friends. There are 6 girls altogether. How might Keenya decide on the number of cookies each can girl gets?
   B. Keenya thinks, "I have about 24 cookies. Since 6×4 is 24, each of us gets 4 cookies." What is Keenya's convenient number? How did she pick it?

2. Jackie's Girl Scout troop is planning a hike. The troop needs to know how heavy the supplies will be. Jackie weighs a bottle of water and finds that it weighs 4.1 kg. About how much will 3 bottles of water weigh?

　　　　　　　　Estimation

Student Guide - Page 202

In *Question 4,* students are asked to estimate the answer to 27 × 6. Three appropriate estimates are provided—120, 150, and 180. Students may arrive at these estimates if they use the convenient numbers 20, 25, or 30, respectively. Since we do not know what the information will be used for, all three estimates are appropriate. If the estimate was calculated in order to determine the number of buses needed to transport students on a field trip, we might want to overestimate and use 180. This would ensure everyone a seat and would allow room for chaperones. On the other hand, it might make sense to use the low estimate if, for example, we need the estimate to determine how many boxes of candy to order for a fund-raiser. If underestimated, the school can always order more candy. If overestimated, the school may have to pay for any unsold candy.

You can assign *Questions 1–7* in the Homework section of the *Estimation* Activity Pages at this time.

Part 2. Estimating Mileage

Ask students to turn to the map and mileage chart that accompany *Questions 8–15* on the *Estimation* Activity Pages. Ask:

- *Locate Chicago, Indianapolis, Louisville, and St. Louis on the map.*

- *Which two cities listed in the chart are about the same distance from Chicago?* (Both St. Louis and Louisville are about 300 miles from Chicago. The distances on the map should be about the same length. Students can measure with a ruler to check.)

- *Look at the scale on the map. Find two cities that are about 150 miles apart.* (Chicago and Madison) *200 miles apart* (Springfield and Jefferson City)

Questions 8–15 should be done in groups. Encourage students to use differernt strategies to solve the problems and to share their strategies in a full class discussion. Discuss what convenient or round numbers they used in their mental calculations.

For *Question 8A* students read the mileage chart to find the distance between Chicago and Indianapolis and then choose two convenient numbers to use for 179. Then, in *Question 9* they use the convenient number to estimate the number of miles driven round-trip from Chicago to Indianapolis. Some students might round 179 to 180 and then double 180 to get 360 miles. Others might choose the convenient number of 200. Doubling 200 gives an estimate of 400 miles.

We find estimates when we need to have a good idea about how big or small a number is, but we do not need to know exactly. Sometimes it is impossible to know an exact answer. We use estimates in many different situations.

For example:
You can estimate how far you live from Boston or Chicago.
You can estimate how many people are watching a Little League game.
You can estimate how much you will pay for a full cart of groceries.

When we estimate, we find a number or answer that is reasonably close to the actual number. It may be bigger or smaller than the actual number, depending on the problem. To make an estimate, we sometimes need to do some number operations in our head. To make these computations easy to do in our heads, we often choose **convenient numbers** to make our estimates. Convenient numbers are really estimates as well.

Which of the answers in Questions 3 and 4 are reasonable estimates? There may be more than one reasonable answer. When is one estimate better than another? Which answers are unreasonable?

3. Mrs. Borko buys 4 jackets for her children. Each jacket costs $47. About how much will all 4 jackets cost?

   A. $100   B. $20   C. $160   D. $2000   E. $200

4. There are about 27 students in each fourth-grade class at Hill Street Elementary School. If there are 6 fourth-grade classes, how many fourth-graders are there at the school?

   A. 120   B. 1200   C. 150   D. 180   E. 300

5. Keenya and her sister went to a concert in the park with her parents. People sat in rows on benches. Keenya counted 12 people in the first row. There were 9 rows.

   A. Keenya thought, "There are about 10 people in each of the 9 rows. There are about..." Finish Keenya's statement using 10 as a convenient number.

   B. Keenya's sister thought, "There are about 10 rows and about 10 people in each row. I'd say there are about..." Finish her statement. What convenient numbers did Keenya's sister use to make her estimate?

6. At the grocery store, Jackie and her brother pick some grapes and weigh them. The grapes weigh 3 pounds and 7 ounces. Grapes are on sale for 49¢ a pound (1 pound = 16 ounces). Jackie and her brother estimate the price of the grapes.

   A. Jackie thinks, "3 pounds and 7 ounces is about 4 pounds. 4 pounds of grapes, at 50¢ a pound, would be..." Finish Jackie's statement. Will the actual price be higher or lower than this estimate?

Estimation   SG · Grade 4 · Unit 7 · Lesson 6   203

Student Guide - Page 203

B. Jackie's brother thinks, "3 pounds of grapes cost 3 × 50¢ or $1.50. 7 ounces is about ½ pound. If 1 pound costs 50¢, ½ pound costs about 25¢. The grapes we picked should cost about..." Finish his statement.

C. If Jackie and her brother want to be sure they have enough money for the grapes, whose estimate would be better to use? Why do you think so?

7. Michael's father travels 36 miles to work every day.

   A. About how many miles does he travel to and from work in one week (5 days)? Solve this problem in your head. Then, explain how you solved it. Be sure to tell what convenient numbers you used.

   B. Share your method with a classmate. What convenient numbers did your classmate choose?

Estimating Mileage

Jerome and his family are thinking about taking a vacation. Jerome found a mileage chart.

	Chicago	Indianapolis	Louisville	St. Louis
Chicago	×	179	294	302
Indianapolis	179	×	112	257
Louisville	294	112	×	275
St. Louis	302	257	275	×

0 150 300 450 miles

8. A. How far is it from Chicago to Indianapolis?
   B. Give two possible convenient numbers for this distance.

9. About how many miles will they travel if Jerome's family drives from Chicago to Indianapolis, and then back home to Chicago?

10. A. Which drive is longer: the drive from Chicago to Indianapolis or the drive from Indianapolis to St. Louis?
    B. About how much longer?

204 SG · Grade 4 · Unit 7 · Lesson 6   Estimation

Student Guide - Page 204

Question 10 involves a subtraction problem. To estimate the answer to $257 - 179$, some students might use 260 and 200, respectively, while others choose 250 and 180 or 250 and 175. Students' choices for convenient numbers will depend on their fluency with subtraction facts.

Questions 11–12 require students to estimate the answer to addition problems involving three addends. Suggest that students record the convenient numbers as they read the mileage chart, instead of trying to store all three numbers in their heads. **Questions 13–15** involve multiplication problems. Encourage students to record the convenient numbers they choose to solve each problem.

Suggestions for Teaching the Lesson

Homework and Practice

- Homework is included in the *Student Guide*. Assign **Questions 1–7** of the Homework section after Part 1 of this lesson and **Questions 8–13** after Part 2.

- DPP item W practices computational estimation. Challenge X develops number sense with money and negative numbers. Task Z provides more practice with multiplication.

Daily Practice and Problems:
Task and Challenge for Lesson 6

X. Challenge: Savings
(URG p. 22)

On Monday, the balance in Nicholas's checking account was $10.

1. On Tuesday, he wrote a check for $25. What was his new balance?

2. On Wednesday, he deposited $50. What was his new balance?

3. On Thursday, he wrote two checks for $20 each. What was his new balance?

4. On Friday, he deposited $25. What was his new balance?

Z. Task: Multiplication (URG p. 23)

Use paper and pencil or mental math to solve the following problems. Estimate to see if your answers are reasonable.

1. A. $43 \times 7 =$

   B. $85 \times 7 =$

   C. $62 \times 8 =$

   D. $67 \times 6 =$

   E. $96 \times 4 =$

   F. $79 \times 5 =$

2. Solve Question 1F a different way. Describe both strategies.

---

11. First, Jerome's family plans on taking the following trip: Chicago to Louisville, Louisville to St. Louis, and St. Louis back home to Chicago. About how many miles is this trip?

12. Jerome's family changes plans. They decide on the following trip: Chicago to Indianapolis, Indianapolis to Louisville, and Louisville back home to Chicago. About how many miles will they drive altogether?

13. Their car goes about 21 miles on one gallon of gasoline. At the start of the trip, their gas tank has about 12 gallons of gas.
    A. About how many miles can they travel on 12 gallons of gas?
    B. Will they have to get more gas before they reach Indianapolis? Before they reach Louisville?

14. At the time they were leaving, gasoline cost about $1.69 per gallon in Chicago. They estimated that they would need about 28 gallons of gas in all to make the trip. If gas costs about the same in other cities as in Chicago, about how much money will they spend for gas on the trip?

15. Jerome's parents averaged 48 miles per hour on the entire trip. By the time they got back to Chicago, did the family drive for more or less than 8 hours? How did you decide?

Homework

Estimate answers to these problems. Be ready to tell how you used convenient numbers.

1. Ana found 12 tomatoes on one tomato plant. Ana has 11 tomato plants. If all the plants have about the same number of tomatoes, about how many tomatoes do the plants have altogether?

2. A box of crackers weighs 269 grams. About how much do 5 boxes of crackers weigh together?

3. If a pizza costs $3.75, a bag of apples $2.50, and a quart of milk $.80, about how much money is needed to buy one of each?

4. If a pizza costs $3.75, about how much will 3 pizzas cost?

5. Jacob's brother works at a fast-food restaurant and earns $5.15 an hour. If he worked 20 hours one week, about how much money did he earn?

6. Tanya earned $5.45 baby-sitting on Monday and $8.70 on Tuesday. She spent $6.65 of this money on Wednesday. About how much money does she have left?

Estimation   SG · Grade 4 · Unit 7 · Lesson 6   205

Student Guide - Page 205

Assessment

- *Questions 1–7* of the Homework section can be used for assessment. Review the TIMS Student Rubric: *Solving* with the class. Students can explain their answers either orally or in writing. They should tell how they solved the problems and what convenient numbers they used.

- Use DPP item Y to assess students' abilities to multiply numbers with ending zeros.

- Use the *Observational Assessment Record* to record students' abilities to use convenient numbers to estimate sums, differences, and products.

7. Mount McKinley in Alaska is the highest mountain in the United States. It is 20,320 feet above sea level. The highest mountain in the 48 contiguous states (all the states except Alaska and Hawaii) is Mount Whitney in California. Mount Whitney is 14,494 feet above sea level. About how much higher is Mount McKinley than Mount Whitney?

Use the map below to answer Questions 8–13.

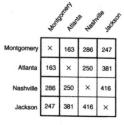

	Montgomery	Atlanta	Nashville	Jackson
Montgomery	×	163	286	247
Atlanta	163	×	250	381
Nashville	286	250	×	416
Jackson	247	381	416	×

0   150   300   450 miles

8. A. How far is it from Montgomery, Alabama, to Jackson, Mississippi?
    B. What is a convenient number to use in place of this number?

9. A. How far is it from Nashville, Tennessee, to Montgomery, Alabama?
    B. What is a convenient number to use in place of this number?

10. About how many miles is a drive from Nashville, Tennessee, to Montgomery, Alabama, and back home to Nashville?

11. A. Which drive is longer: a drive from Montgomery to Nashville or a drive from Montgomery to Jackson?
    B. About how much longer?

12. About how long is the following trip: from Jackson to Montgomery, from Montgomery to Nashville, and then Nashville back home to Jackson?

13. About how long is the following trip: from Atlanta to Montgomery, Montgomery to Jackson, and Jackson back home to Atlanta?

206 SG · Grade 4 · Unit 7 · Lesson 6   Estimation

Student Guide - Page 206

AT A GLANCE

Math Facts and Daily Practice and Problems

DPP item W provides estimation practice. Challenge X uses positive and negative numbers in a problem involving money. Bit Y provides practice multiplying numbers with ending zeros. Task Z provides practice in multiplication.

Part 1. Estimating with Multiplication

1. Discuss situations when an estimate is a good answer.
2. Discuss finding convenient numbers as a step in estimating.
3. Discuss how different situations call for different convenient numbers.
4. Students read the introduction on the *Estimation* Activity Pages in the *Student Guide.*
5. Discuss *Questions 1–7* in the *Student Guide.*

Part 2. Estimating Mileage

1. Familiarize students with the mileage chart and map that accompany *Questions 8–15.*
2. In groups, students solve *Questions 8–15.*

Homework

Students complete *Questions 1–7* in the Homework section of the *Estimation* Activity Pages after Part 1 of this lesson and *Questions 8–13* after Part 2.

Assessment

1. Use DPP item Y as an assessment.
2. *Questions 1–7* in the Homework section can be used for assessment. Review the TIMS Student Rubric: *Solving* with the class.
3. Use the *Observational Assessment Record* to record students' abilities to make reasonable estimates.

Notes:

Student Guide

Questions 1–15 (SG pp. 202–205)

See the Content Note in Lesson Guide 6.

1. **A.** Answers will vary. Divide them equally. Each girl gets 4 cookies. One is left over.

   B. 24; She knows the multiplication fact 6×4.

2. About 12 kg

3. *C or E

4. *A, C, or D

5. **A.** 90 people

   B. 100 people; 10 rows of 10 people

6. **A.** $2.00; lower

   B. $1.75

   C. Jackie's estimate; it is higher so they will feel more confident that they have enough money. It is better to overestimate when dealing with money.

7. **A.** Estimates will vary. 350–400 miles

   B. Answers will vary. $70 \times 5 = 350$ miles; $80 \times 5 = 400$ miles

8. **A.** 179 miles

   B. Convenient numbers will vary. 175, 180, or 200 miles

9. *Estimates will vary. 350, 360, or 400 miles

10. **A.** Indianapolis to St. Louis

    B. *Estimates for the subtraction problem $257 - 179$ will vary. About 60–80 miles

11. Estimates for $294 + 275 + 302$ will vary. About 850–900 miles

12. Estimates for $179 + 112 + 294$ will vary. About 575–610 miles

13. **A.** Estimates will vary. About 200–260 miles.

    B. No; Chicago to Indianapolis is 179 miles. They can travel more than 200 miles on their tank of gas. They will need gas on their way from Indianapolis to Louisville.

14. Estimates will vary. $45–$60

15. More; Driving 8 hours at 48 miles per hour is about 400 miles. Their trip is about 600 miles. They must have driven for longer than 8 hours.

Homework (SG pp. 205–206)

Questions 1–13

Answers will vary.

1. About 100–130 tomatoes

2. 1250–1500 grams

3. $7–$8

4. $11–$12

5. About $100

6. $7–$8

7. About 5000–6000 feet

8. **A.** 247 miles

   B. 200, 240, 250 miles

9. **A.** 286 miles

   B. 250, 280, 285, 290, 300 miles

10. About 500–600 miles

11. **A.** Montgomery to Nashville

    B. Estimates for the subtraction problem $286 - 247$ will vary. 35–50 miles

12. Estimates for $247 + 286 + 416$ will vary. 900–1000 miles

13. Estimates for $163 + 247 + 381$ will vary. 760–830 miles

---

*Answers and/or discussion are included in the Lesson Guide.

**Answers for all the Home Practice in the *Discovery Assignment Book* are at the end of the unit.

AA. Multiplication Quiz: Last Six Facts
(URG p. 23)

A. $8 \times 6 =$

B. $6 \times 4 =$

C. $4 \times 7 =$

D. $7 \times 8 =$

E. $6 \times 7 =$

F. $8 \times 4 =$

DPP Task is on page 89. Suggestions for using the DPPs are on page 89.

LESSON GUIDE 7

Multiplying Round Numbers

| Estimated Class Sessions: 1 | Multiplying by multiples of ten is expanded in this lesson. Students use patterns involving multiplying multidigit numbers that end in zeros. Students |

practice estimating.

Key Content

*   Multiplying multidigit numbers with ending zeros.
*   Estimating products.

Materials List

Print Materials for Students

		Math Facts and Daily Practice and Problems	Activity	Homework	Written Assessment
Student Books	Student Guide		*Multiplying Round Numbers* Pages 207–209	*Multiplying Round Numbers* Homework Section Pages 209–210	
	Discovery Assignment Book			Home Practice Part 6 Page 87	
Teacher Resources	Facts Resource Guide	DPP Item 7AA			DPP Item 7AA *Multiplication Quiz: Last Six Facts*
	Unit Resource Guide	DPP Items AA–BB Pages 23–24			DPP Item AA *Multiplication Quiz: Last Six Facts* Page 23 and *Multiplication* Page 90, 1 per student

(◎) available on Teacher Resource CD

All Transparency Masters, Blackline Masters, and Assessment Blackline Masters in the Unit Resource Guide are on the Teacher Resource CD.

Supplies for Each Student

calculator

Developing the Activity

Ask students to read the opening vignette in the *Multiplying Round Numbers* Activity Pages in the *Student Guide*. Make sure students understand that small flowers for planting often come in trays. In this case, we assumed a tray of 48 flowers. Students estimate how many flowers are in 28 trays. Sophia suggests using the convenient numbers 50 (for the 48 flowers per tray) and 30 (for the 28 trays).

In order to compute 50×30 in **Question 2,** students look for patterns in multiplying:

$$5 \times 3$$
$$5 \times 30$$
$$50 \times 3$$
$$50 \times 30$$
$$500 \times 30, \text{etc.}$$

Explore these products with your class. Students should use their calculators to compute the products. Ask:

- *Do you see a pattern?*
- *Can you predict the number of zeros in the product before doing the calculation? How?*

Students should agree that there are about 1500 flowers on a shelf.

With your class, think of other ways to find 50×30 **(Question 4).** One way is to skip count by 50s. In order not to get lost, instead of skip counting by 50 thirty times, skip counting 10 times may be helpful (50, 100, 150, . . . 500). Since $30 = 10 \times 3$, $50 \times 30 = 50 \times 10 \times 3$, and we can add $500 + 500 + 500$ for a total of 1500. There are many other ways to think about 50×30. Give students a chance to explore these options.

Question 5 asks students to multiply 2-digit numbers, where both numbers are multiples of ten. Students should discover that the product will have at least 2 zeros. The product 40×50 contains 3 since $4 \times 5 = 20$.

Work through the *Multiplying Round Numbers* Activity Pages allowing students to work independently or in groups first and then going over the problems as a class.

Multiplying Round Numbers

The Beautiful Blooms Garden Store sells many trays of flowers. A tray of flowers has 6 rows. There are 8 flowers in each row.

1. How many flowers are in each tray?

Ana and Grace went to the Beautiful Blooms Garden Store. They noticed that the trays of flowers were stored on a shelf. Ana counted 28 trays on a shelf.

Ana said, "I wonder how many flowers are on one of these shelves."

Grace replied, "We can estimate the number of flowers on a shelf: 48 flowers is about 50 and 28 trays is about 30 trays. So what is 50×30?"

28 trays of flowers on a shelf

2. Ana learned that patterns often help us multiply. Find the following products using a calculator if needed. Describe any patterns you see.
   - A. $5 \times 3 =$
   - B. $5 \times 30 =$
   - C. $50 \times 3 =$
   - D. $50 \times 30 =$
   - E. $50 \times 300 =$
   - F. $500 \times 30 =$
   - G. $500 \times 300 =$

3. About how many flowers did Ana and Grace see on a shelf?

4. Discuss other ways to compute 50×30.

Student Guide - Page 207

---

5. Find the following pairs of products in your head. Check your work on a calculator if needed.

A.	80 ×2	80 ×20	B.	20 ×4	20 ×40	C.	50 ×7	50 ×70
D.	90 ×7	90 ×70	E.	70 ×1	70 ×10	F.	30 ×6	30 ×60

G. $90 \times 20 =$ H. $40 \times 50 =$ I. $60 \times 40 =$

6. A. Ana and Grace counted 10 shelves of marigolds. If there are 28 trays on each shelf, about how many trays of marigolds are there?

Grace said, "Wow, there's a lot of marigolds here. There are 10 shelves and about 30 trays on each shelf. Since $10 \times 30 = 300$, I estimated 300 trays of marigolds."

28 trays on each of 10 shelves is about 10×30 or 300 trays.

B. Ana said, "If each tray has about 50 flowers and there are about 300 trays, that means there are $50 \times 300 = 15,000$ marigolds. That's amazing!"

300 trays with about 50 flowers on each is 50×300 or 15,000 marigolds.

What is another way to estimate the total number of flowers?

Find the following products with your calculator. Look for patterns.

7.	$4 \times 7 =$	8.	$6 \times 7 =$	9.	$8 \times 5 =$
	$40 \times 7 =$		$60 \times 7 =$		$80 \times 5 =$
	$4 \times 70 =$		$6 \times 70 =$		$8 \times 50 =$
	$40 \times 70 =$		$60 \times 70 =$		$80 \times 50 =$
	$400 \times 70 =$		$600 \times 70 =$		$800 \times 50 =$
	$40 \times 700 =$		$60 \times 700 =$		$80 \times 500 =$
	$400 \times 700 =$		$600 \times 700 =$		$800 \times 500 =$

Student Guide - Page 208

10. Ana says she can multiply 40 × 40 in her head easily. What method do you think Ana is using? What is 40 × 40?

11. Ana saw that for every zero in the factors, there is a zero in the product. Do you agree? Explain.

12. Grace says multiplying 400 × 50 is tricky. What is 400 × 50? Why is it tricky?

In Question 6, Ana and Grace used convenient numbers to estimate the number of flowers they saw.

For Questions 13–18, complete steps A and B.

    A. Estimate the following products in your head by finding convenient numbers. Be prepared to share your strategies.

    B. Use a calculator to compute the product. Then, use your estimate to see if your answer is reasonable.

13. 32 × 6 =   14. 4 × 67 =   15. 8 × 99 =

16. 30 × 41 =   17. 40 × 49 =   18. 300 × 24 =

19. Describe a way to compute the exact product in your head in Question 15 without using a calculator or pencil and paper.

Homework

Find the products using mental computation.

1. 40 ×70	2. 60 ×60	3. 500 ×60	4. 800 ×30	5. 300 ×30
6. 100 ×100	7. 600 ×40	8. 400 ×200	9. 2000 ×800	10. 6000 ×700

11. Explain how to multiply two numbers that end in zeros.

For Questions 12–24, estimate the products using convenient numbers.

12. 42 ×8   13. 76 ×4   14. 69 ×7

15. Describe a way to compute the exact product in Question 14 using mental math.

Student Guide - Page 209

---

16. 60 × 34 =   17. 50 × 79 =   18. 320 × 70 =   19. 496 × 90 =

The Bessie Coleman Parent Teacher Committee (PTC) decided to plant a garden by the school.

20. If there are about 38 daisies in a flat and 23 families each donate a flat of daisies to the garden, about how many daisy plants were donated?

21. The PTC bought 32 trays of assorted flowers. Each tray contains 48 flowers. About how many plants did the PTC buy?

22. A rose bush costs $6.89. The PTC bought 18 bushes. About how much did the PTC spend on rose bushes?

23. The PTC bought 35 bags of top soil. Each bag weighs 40 pounds. About how many pounds of top soil did they buy?

24. The PTC held a fun fair to help with the cost of the garden. Adult tickets cost $5.75 and children's tickets cost $2.25. The PTC sold 89 adult tickets and 112 children's tickets. About how much money did they make?

Student Guide - Page 210

Questions 6–9 look at patterns and strategies for solving multiplication problems with zeros.

Discuss patterns in the zeros ***(Questions 10–12).*** Students will eventually see that the product of two numbers ending in zeros will have as many zeros as the factors: 30 × 500 = 15,000. There are 3 zeros in the factors and 3 in the product. However, there may be one more zero than in the factors. For example, 40 × 500 = 20,000 has four zeros. One of the zeros comes from 4 × 5 = 20.

Questions 13–19 require students to find convenient numbers. Students should, for the most part, use convenient numbers that contain one non-zero digit followed by zeros. Other convenient numbers are possible, however. For example, in ***Question 18,*** students may use 300 × 25. Discuss the various estimates students suggest.

 TIMS Tip

The activities in this lesson provide good opportunities for reading large numbers.

Journal Prompt

Write a letter to a friend explaining how many zeros are in 600 × 50.

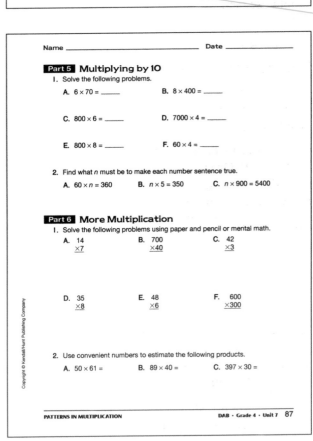

Name _____   Date _____

Part 5 **Multiplying by 10**

1. Solve the following problems.

  A. 6 × 70 = _____   B. 8 × 400 = _____

  C. 800 × 6 = _____   D. 7000 × 4 = _____

  E. 800 × 8 = _____   F. 60 × 4 = _____

2. Find what *n* must be to make each number sentence true.

  A. 60 × *n* = 360   B. *n* × 5 = 350   C. *n* × 900 = 5400

Part 6 **More Multiplication**

1. Solve the following problems using paper and pencil or mental math.

  A. 14 ×7   B. 700 ×40   C. 42 ×3

  D. 35 ×8   E. 48 ×6   F. 600 ×300

2. Use convenient numbers to estimate the following products.

  A. 50 × 61 =   B. 89 × 40 =   C. 397 × 30 =

Discovery Assignment Book - Page 87

Suggestions for Teaching the Lesson

Homework and Practice

- Assign the Homework section in the *Student Guide*.
- Assign DPP Task BB which reviews area and perimeter of shapes.
- Assign Part 6 of the Home Practice.

Answers for Part 6 of the Home Practice can be found in the Answer Key at the end of this lesson and at the end of this unit.

Assessment

- DPP item AA is a quiz on the last six multiplication facts.
- Use the *Multiplication* Assessment Blackline Master to assess students' abilities to solve multiplication problems.

Daily Practice and Problems: Task for Lesson 7

BB. Task: Area and Perimeter
(URG p. 24)

1. What is the area of the shape below?

2. What is the perimeter?

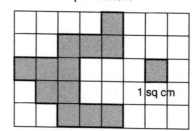

1 sq cm

3. Draw a shape on *Centimeter Grid Paper* that has twice the area of the shape above. What is the perimeter of your shape?

AT A GLANCE

Math Facts and Daily Practice and Problems

DPP item AA is a quiz on the last six multiplication facts. Task BB reviews finding the area and perimeter of shapes.

Developing the Activity

1. Discuss the opening vignette on the *Multiplying Round Numbers* Activity Pages in the *Student Guide* that gives a context for 50×30.
2. Students explore multiplying multidigit numbers that end in zeros.
3. Students complete *Questions 1–5* on the *Multiplying Round Numbers* Activity Pages in groups and discuss them as a class.
4. Students work on *Questions 6–12* independently or in groups. They then discuss convenient numbers in *Questions 13–19*.

Homework

1. Assign the Homework section in the *Student Guide*.
2. Assign Part 6 of the Home Practice to review multiplication.

Assessment

1. DPP item AA is a multiplication facts quiz.
2. Students complete the *Multiplication* Assessment Page.

Notes:

Multiplication

Use mental math to solve the problems in Questions 1–4.

1. $\begin{array}{r} 60 \\ \times 4 \\ \hline \end{array}$

2. $\begin{array}{r} 50 \\ \times 9 \\ \hline \end{array}$

3. $\begin{array}{r} 600 \\ \times 7 \\ \hline \end{array}$

4. $\begin{array}{r} 900 \\ \times 80 \\ \hline \end{array}$

Find exact answers to Questions 5–7. Estimate to see if your answer is reasonable.

5. $63 \times 2 =$

6. $45 \times 6 =$

7. $\begin{array}{r} 37 \\ \times 5 \\ \hline \end{array}$

8. Explain your estimation strategy for Question 7.

Find *n* to make the sentences true.

9. $700 \times 7 = n$

10. $n \times 2500 = 5000$

11. $3 \times n = 18,000$

Student Guide

Questions 1–19 (SG pp. 207–209)

1. 48 flowers
2. **A.** 15
   B. 150
   C. 150
   D. 1500
   E. 15,000
   F. 15,000
   G. 150,000

Students may see that the number of zeros in the product is equal to the number of zeros in the multiplicands.

3. Estimates will vary. An estimate based on Grace's convenient numbers is 1500 flowers.
4. *See the Lesson Guide for a discussion.
5. **A.** 160; 1600
   B. 80; 800
   C. 350; 3500
   D. 630; 6300
   E. 70; 700
   F. 180; 1800
   G. 1800
   H. 2000
   I. 2400
6. **A.** Estimates will vary. An estimate based on the convenient number Grace used is 300 trays.
   B. Answers will vary. Ana and Grace estimated that the number of flowers on one shelf is about 1500 flowers. (See **Question 3.**) Since there are 10 shelves, multiply 1500 by 10 to get an estimate of 15,000 flowers.
7. 28; 280; 280; 2800; 28,000; 28,000; 280,000
8. 42; 420; 420; 4200; 42,000; 42,000; 420,000
9. 40; 400; 400; 4000; 40,000; 40,000; 400,000
10. Answers will vary. 1600. Ana might multiply 4×4 to get 16 and add on two zeros.

11. Yes, but there may be more zeros if the problem involves multiplication facts that have products that are multiples of 10.
12. 20,000. An extra zero is made by multiplying $4 \times 5 = 20$.
13. **A.** Estimates will vary. One possible estimate is 180.
    B. 192
14. **A.** Estimates will vary. One possible estimate is 280.
    B. 268
15. **A.** Estimates will vary. One possible estimate is 800.
    B. 792
16. **A.** Estimates will vary. One possible estimate is 1200.
    B. 1230
17. **A.** Estimates will vary. One possible estimate is 2000.
    B. 1960
18. **A.** Estimates will vary. Possible estimates are 6000 or 7500.
    B. 7200
19. Descriptions will vary. Students might multiply $8 \times 100 - 8 = 792$.

Homework (SG pp. 209–210)

Questions 1–24

1. 2800
2. 3600
3. 30,000
4. 24,000
5. 9000
6. 10,000
7. 24,000
8. 80,000
9. 1,600,000
10. 4,200,000

---

*Answers and/or discussion are included in the Lesson Guide.
**Answers for all the Home Practice in the *Discovery Assignment Book* are at the end of the unit.

11. Explanations will vary. Students can multiply the numbers in the largest place, then count the numbers of zeros in the factors and add them to the product of the numbers in the largest place.

Estimates will vary for *Questions 12–24.* One possible solution is given for each.

12. $40 \times 8 = 320$
13. $4 \times 80 = 320$
14. $7 \times 70 = 490$
15. $70 \times 7 - 7 = 483$
16. $60 \times 30 = 1800; 60 \times 40 = 2400;$ Between 1800 and 2400.
17. $50 \times 80 = 4000.$
18. $300 \times 70 = 21,000.$
19. $500 \times 90 = 45,000.$
20. $40 \times 20 = 800$ daisies.
21. $30 \times 50 = 1500$ flowers.
22. $\$7.00 \times 20 = \$140.$
23. $30 \times 40 = 1200$ pounds; $40 \times 40 = 1600$ pounds; Between 1200 and 1600.
24. $90 \times \$6 + 100 \times \$2 = \$540 + \$200 = \$740.$

Unit Resource Guide

Multiplication (URG p. 90)

Questions 1–11

1. 240
2. 450
3. 4200
4. 72,000
5. 126
6. 270
7. 185
8. Strategies will vary. Possible strategy: Product is between $5 \times 30 = 150$ and $5 \times 40 = 200.$
9. 4900
10. 2
11. 6000

Discovery Assignment Book

Home Practice (DAB p. 87)

Part 6. More Multiplication

Questions 1–2

1. A. 98
   B. 28,000
   C. 126
   D. 280
   E. 288
   F. 180,000
2. A. One possible estimate: 3000
   B. One possible estimate: 3600
   C. One possible estimate: 12,000

*Answers and/or discussion are included in the Lesson Guide.

**Answers for all the Home Practice in the *Discovery Assignment Book* are at the end of the unit.

LESSON GUIDE

A Camping Trip

This lesson is a series of word problems requiring estimation and computation.

Key Content

- Solving multistep word problems.
- Solving problems involving multiplication.
- Choosing whether to estimate or find an exact answer.
- Connecting mathematics to real-life situations.
- Communicating solutions verbally and in writing.

Daily Practice and Problems: Bit for Lesson 8

CC. More Multiplication (URG p. 24)

Use paper and pencil or mental math to solve the following problems. Estimate to be sure your answer is reasonable.

1. A. 47×9

   B. 64×8

2. Explain your estimation strategy for Question 1B.

DPP Challenge is on page 95. Suggestions for using the DPPs are on page 95.

Materials List

Print Materials for Students

	Math Facts and Daily Practice and Problems	Activity	Written Assessment
Student Books — Student Guide		*A Camping Trip* Pages 211–213	
Student Books — Discovery Assignment Book			Home Practice Part 7 Page 88
Teacher Resource — Unit Resource Guide	DPP Items CC–DD Pages 24–25 ⊙		

⊙ *available on Teacher Resource CD*

All Transparency Masters, Blackline Masters, and Assessment Blackline Masters in the Unit Resource Guide are on the Teacher Resource CD.

Materials for the Teacher

Observational Assessment Record (Unit Resource Guide, Pages 7–8 and Teacher Resource CD)
Individual Assessment Record Sheet (Teacher Implementation Guide, Assessment section and Teacher Resource CD)

A Camping Trip

Estimate, then solve each problem. Use your estimate to check whether your solution is reasonable.

Ana and her family are going camping at the Potawatomi (POD-A-WAD-TO-MI) State Park in Wisconsin. The fee to camp in the park is $12.00 a night for families who live in Wisconsin and $16.00 a night for people who do not live in Wisconsin.

1. Ana's family is arriving on Tuesday and staying until Sunday afternoon. Ana's family lives in Illinois. How much does Ana's family have to pay?

2. Nadia, a fourth grader from Milwaukee, Wisconsin, is also camping from Tuesday until Sunday. How much does Nadia's family pay to stay at the park?

3. How much more does Ana's family pay than Nadia's?

POTAWATOMI STATE PARK
CAMPING FEES
$12.00/night
Wisconsin residents
$16.00/night
non-residents

A campground is a big area where many people can pitch their tents. A campground is divided into campsites. Each family that camps at the park gets a campsite.

A Camping Trip   SG · Grade 4 · Unit 7 · Lesson 8 211

Student Guide - Page 211

4. There are 4 campgrounds in the park. Each campground has 120 campsites. How many families can stay at the park at one time?

5. Ana, who is 10 years old, her 12-year-old brother Felipe, and Dalia, her 5-year-old sister, want to explore the park. Their father and mother ask them to help put up the tent. Dalia looked at her watch when they began. It was 2:06. They finished setting up the tent at 2:52. How long did it take them to set up the tent?

6. One evening, Ana's family ate dinner at a restaurant in a nearby town. The restaurant had an "all-you-can-eat" fish dinner. The cost is $7.00 for adults, $5.00 for children ages 6–11, and $2.50 for children ages 3–5. If the whole family orders the fish dinner, how much will the total bill be?

Ana's 11-year-old cousin Roberto, his mother, and his little sister Angela come to the park on Friday. They set up their tent at a nearby campsite. The families decide to go canoeing together. It costs $8.00 to rent a canoe for 1 hour. Each canoe holds 3 people.

7. Every person who is in a boat needs a life jacket. How many adult life jackets do they need? (Adults are ages 12 and up.) How many children's life jackets do they need?

8. How many canoes will they need to rent? There must be at least one adult in every canoe. (Adults are ages 12 and up.) Draw a picture of how Ana's and Roberto's families can seat themselves in the canoes.

9. How much will they have to pay if they canoe for 1 hour?

10. How much will they have to pay if they canoe for 2 hours?

212 SG · Grade 4 · Unit 7 · Lesson 8   A Camping Trip

Student Guide - Page 212

11. A. After canoeing, Ana's and Roberto's families decide to stop for frozen yogurt at the snack shop. A single-dip cone is 69¢. The price includes tax. Estimate how much money is needed to buy a cone for every person in both families.

    B. Ana gives the cashier $10.00 to pay for all the cones. About how much change will she get back?

12. The families decide to go on a long hike Saturday morning. Ana's father brought ingredients to make gorp. Gorp is a high-energy snack that is easy to take on a hike. Here is his recipe for 4 servings of gorp:

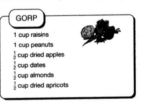

GORP

1 cup raisins
1 cup peanuts
$\frac{1}{2}$ cup dried apples
$\frac{3}{4}$ cup dates
$\frac{1}{2}$ cup almonds
$\frac{1}{2}$ cup dried apricots

Ana's father wants to make a serving of gorp for everybody who went camping. How many servings of gorp does he need to make?

13. How many cups of peanuts should he use?

14. How many cups of dried apricots should he use?

15. Driving home from their vacation, Roberto's mother says they will travel about 50 miles in 1 hour. It takes them about 6 hours to get home. About how far is the park from their home?

16. Make up a story for the multiplication problems below and solve the problem. Your story can be about camping or anything else.

    12   8 $1.75
    ×8   ×6   ×8

A Camping Trip   SG · Grade 4 · Unit 7 · Lesson 8 213

Student Guide - Page 213

Students solve a series of word problems that practice skills and concepts from this and previous units. The problems can be used in several ways. Students can work on the problems individually at first and then to come together in pairs or small groups to compare solutions. Then the group's solutions can be shared with others in a class discussion. The problems can also be assigned for homework. Because this activity does not require much teacher preparation, it is appropriate to leave for a substitute teacher.

Suggestions for Teaching the Lesson

Homework and Practice

- Assign some or all of the questions on the *A Camping Trip* Activity Pages in the *Student Guide* for homework.
- DPP Bit CC provides multiplication practice.

Assessment

- Use the *Observational Assessment Record* to document students' abilities to solve problems involving multiplication. Transfer appropriate information from the Unit 7 *Observational Assessment Record* to students' *Individual Assessment Record Sheets*.
- Use Home Practice Part 7 to assess students' multiplication and problem-solving skills.

Answers for Part 7 of the Home Practice can be found in the Answer Key at the end of this lesson and at the end of this unit.

Extension

DPP Challenge DD provides practice using 10% as a standard for error analysis. Use this item with students who completed Lesson 5 *Close Enough* in Unit 6.

Daily Practice and Problems: Challenge for Lesson 8

DD. Challenge: Within 10%: Area
(URG p. 25)

Shannon is getting new carpet in her room. She estimated that her bedroom floor has an area of 120 square feet. When she measured her room, she found that the area is 130 square feet.

1. Is her estimate within 10% of the actual area?

2. Is her estimate of 120 square feet a good one for ordering carpet? Why or why not?

Name _____ Date _____

Part 7 Groups and More Groups

1. Solve the following problems using paper and pencil or mental math.

   A. 53   B. 38   C. 77   D. 65
       ×4   ×2   ×3   ×5

2. Bessie Coleman School is holding a fund-raiser. The money earned will go towards buying new books for the school library. Jacob is in charge of pouring lemonade at the fund-raiser. He has 19 packages of paper cups. Each package has 20 cups. About how many cups does he have?

3. Lee Yah is in charge of selling hot dogs. She has 36 packages of hot dog buns at the start of the day. Each package has 8 buns. How many hot dogs can she sell?

4. Jacob is selling raffle tickets. One raffle ticket sells for $4.
   A. So far he has collected $160. How many raffle tickets did he sell?

   B. His goal is to collect $400. How many more raffle tickets must he sell to reach his goal?

5. Ten people can sit at one table for Bingo. There are 12 tables for Bingo. How many people can play Bingo at one time?

6. At the fund-raiser, a "meal deal" that includes a hot dog, drink, and chips costs $3. There are 96 students in the eighth grade at Bessie Coleman School. If each eighth grader buys one meal deal, how much money will the eighth grade class pay in all for their food?

88   DAB · Grade 4 · Unit 7   PATTERNS IN MULTIPLICATION

Discovery Assignment Book - Page 88

URG · Grade 4 · Unit 7 · Lesson 8   95

AT A GLANCE

Math Facts and Daily Practice and Problems

DPP Bit CC practices multiplication skills. Challenge DD reviews using 10% as a standard for error analysis.

Developing the Activity

Students solve the word problems in pairs or small groups, then discuss their strategies with the class.

Homework

Assign some or all of the problems for homework.

Assessment

1. Use Home Practice Part 7 as a quiz.
2. Document students' progress solving problems involving multiplication on the *Observational Assessment Record.* Transfer information from the *Observational Assessment Record* to students' *Individual Assessment Record Sheets.*

Notes:

Student Guide

Questions 1–16 (SG pp. 211–213)

1. $80.00
2. $60.00
3. $20.00
4. 480 families
5. 46 minutes
6. $28.50
7. 4 adults, 4 children
8. 3 canoes. Pictures will vary. One adult must be in every canoe. The adults include Ana's mother and father, her brother Felipe, and Roberto's mother. There will be one canoe with two adults in it. The children can be in any canoe so long as there are not more than three people per canoe.
9. $24.00
10. $48.00
11. **A.** Estimates will vary. One possible solution: $8 \times 70¢ = \$5.60$.
    B. Estimates will vary. One possible solution: $\$10 - \$6 = \$4$.
12. 8 servings
13. 2 cups
14. 1 cup
15. About 300 miles.
16. Stories will vary. Solutions are: 96; 48; $14.

Discovery Assignment Book

**Home Practice (DAB p. 88)

Part 7. Groups and More Groups

Questions 1–6

1. **A.** 212
   B. 76
   C. 231
   D. 325
2. Estimates will vary. One possible estimate: 400 cups
3. 288 hotdogs
4. **A.** 40 raffle tickets
   B. 60 more raffle tickets
5. 120 people
6. $288

*Answers and/or discussion are included in the Lesson Guide.
**Answers for all the Home Practice in the *Discovery Assignment Book* are at the end of the unit.

Discovery Assignment Book

Part 2. Order of Operations

Questions 1–2 (DAB p. 85)

1. **A.** 19
   B. 20
   C. 15
   D. 38
   E. 39
   F. 46
   G. 74
   H. 103

2. Answers will vary.

Part 3. Division

Questions 1–5 (DAB p. 86)

1. 85,680; 27,786; 1028; 10,782. Students' explanations will vary. Possible explanations are: all the even numbers are divisible by two or numbers that have a 0, 2, 4, 6, or 8 in the ones' place are divisible by two.

2. 567; 85,680; 27,786; 10,782. Students' explanations will vary. Students might divide each number by 3 and see if there is a remainder or they might add the digits in each number to see if the sum is a multiple of three.

3. 85,680; 27,786; 10,782. Students' explanations will vary. Students should choose all numbers in common between *Questions 1* and *2*. Numbers that are divisible by 2 and 3 are also divisible by 6.

4. 85,680. Students' explanations will vary. Students might say that numbers that have a 0 or a 5 in the ones' place are divisible by 5 and numbers that have a 0 in the ones' place are divisible by 10.

5. 567; 85,680; 10,782. Students' explanations will vary. Students might divide each number by 9 and see if there is a remainder or they might add the digits in each number to see if the sum is a multiple of nine.

Part 4. Addition and Subtraction Practice

Questions A–I (DAB p. 86)

A. 252
B. 378
C. 385
D. 516
E. 207
F. 315
G. 290
H. 239
I. 395

Part 5. Multiplying by 10

Questions 1–2 (DAB p. 87)

1. **A.** 420
   B. 3200
   C. 4800
   D. 28,000
   E. 6400
   F. 240

2. **A.** 6
   B. 70
   C. 6

Answers and/or discussion are included in the Lesson Guide.

Part 6. More Multiplication

Questions 1–2 (DAB p. 87)

1. **A.** 98
   B. 28,000
   C. 126
   D. 280
   E. 288
   F. 180,000
2. **A.** One possible estimate: 3000
   B. One possible estimate: 3600
   C. One possible estimate: 12,000

Part 7. Groups and More Groups

Questions 1–6 (DAB p. 88)

1. **A.** 212
   B. 76
   C. 231
   D. 325
2. Estimates will vary. One possible estimate: 400 cups
3. 288 hotdogs
4. **A.** 40 raffle tickets
   B. 60 more raffle tickets
5. 120 people
6. $288

*Answers and/or discussion are included in the Lesson Guide.